Front and back covers: From a watercolour
by William Clarke Eddington, born
in Worcester, fl. 1861-1885.

A POCKETFUL OF HOPS

HOP GROWING IN THE BROMYARD AREA

THE BROMYARD AND DISTRICT LOCAL HISTORY SOCIETY
BROMYARD
HEREFORDSHIRE
1988

Published by

The Bromyard and District Local History Society

©

ISBN 0 9502068 4 9

Other publications of The Bromyard and District Local History Society:
  *_Bromyard: A Local History_ (1970)
  *_Bromyard Parish Registers_ by E. D. Pearson (1974)
  Bromyard The Day Before Yesterday, A Book of Photographs (1979)
  Whitbourne: A Bishop's Manor by P. Williams (1979)
  Little Cowarne: A Herefordshire Village by J. Hopkinson (1983)
  Herefordshire Under Arms by C. Hopkinson (1985)
  Bromyard: Minster, Manor and Town by P. Williams (1987)
  *Out of print

Printed by
Orphans Press Ltd.,
Leominster, Herefordshire
HR6 8JT

CONTENTS

MAPS

PLANS

DIAGRAMS

GRAPHS

TABLES

ACKNOWLEDGEMENTS

The Bromyard and District Local History Society wishes to thank everyone who has helped with such enthusiasm and generosity to produce *A Pocketful of Hops*. This book would never have been embarked upon had it not been for the need to record some of the fund of knowledge displayed by the late Inett Homes in his talks to the Society; he and Harry Paske have been the major contributors on the history and the growing and drying of hops.

Additional material and local memories have come from Rene Andrews, Jack Blandford, Gilbert Bowler, Neston Capper, Kay Carey, Michael Carey, Eithne Crosskey, Philip Crosskey, Doll Courtney, Margaret Dallow, Daphne Davies, Irene Davies, Vera Davies, Gladys Draper, Layton Edwards, Dorothy Evans, Jack Fowler, Jean Hopkinson, Gilbert Hyde, Joan Leese, Suzanne Lowden, Neil Parker, Ethel Paske, Gwenllian Paske, Mary Essex Potter, Richard Essex Potter, John Pudge, Bill Rollason, Mildred Shepherd, Edith Silcock, Peter Walker, Deborah Waller, Mollie Walwyn, Phyllis Williams, Hester Wright, Lawson Wright, and many others. Eileen Holloway lent the diaries of her husband, the late Ted Holloway of Lower House, Stanford Bishop, and Norah Taber found the photographs to go with them; Marnie Caine and Brenda Swann copied the crop returns in the Public Record Office.

The following individuals and organisations have also provided information and help: B. J. Whitehouse and the staff at Hereford Library; Sue Hubbard and her staff at Hereford Record Office; The Museum of Cider, Hereford; Keith Worsely, Horticultural Adviser with the Agricultural Development and Advisory Service; The Brewers' Society; John Lander and Alan Meredith, English Hops Ltd; Morris Hanbury Jackson Le May Ltd, International Hop Merchants, Factors and Processors; Richard Rayer, hop merchant of Worcester; The Bruff Company; Bill and Phil Wargent; Norman Ham, former marketing manager of Pikes, Sons & Co; R. C. Alford and the staff of A. & E. Pettifer Ltd, Bromyard; and numerous other growers, factors and merchants.

Lack of space has prevented the printing of more than a few of the many letters and photographs that have been received from the Black Country and South Wales, but all the letters, together with photocopies of photographs, have been deposited in the Bromyard Library where they will make a valuable archive for future reference. The Society is grateful to the writers:

L. R. Baker, P. A. Banner, J. M. Baxter, Mrs Beresford, I. Bill, H. Brooker, M. Brown, B. Butler, V. Chilton, D. Cox, F. Craddock, W. Crook, M. Fownes, D. Goodwin, F. Gordon, I. Griffiths, J. Grinsell, E. H. Hall, R. I. C. Hassell, S. Haydon, M. L. Hicklin, D. Horton, B. Howard, J. Hunt, C. James, R. Jennings, B. Johnson, E. Keay, E. Kofack, R. Leith, J. Lingard, E. Lloyd, V. L., D. J. Oliver, J. Owen, C. Palmer, H. E. Palmer, D. Pardoe, W. H. Parish, C. Parkes, H. Parsons, E. Payne, J. Penty, C. Perry, F. Porter, G. D. Price, G. N. Price, P. S. Ray, H. Richardson, J. Scholfield, W. K. Scott, O. Shelton, M. Skidmore, M. Smith, W. C. Smith, D. A. Spinks, T. E. Taylor, C. J. Tyler, B. Wheeler, K. Whetstone.

Most of the other photographs are from the Society's own collection, built up by Daphne Davies and Deborah Waller from, among other sources, unique family prints lent to the Society for copying. The Society is indebted to everyone else who has given us permission to use their photographs, in particular Arthur and Elsie Berry, James Bomford, Leslie Bowcott, Bert Brookes, Basil Butcher, Martin Hewitt, Henry Hodges, Adam Jones, Robert Jones, Anne Orgee, Harry Paske, Madeleine Pudge and Ethel Waldron; Barbara Rhys for the photograph on page 105 from the Miss Wight Collection in Hereford Record Office; Hereford City Museum for the photograph on page 6 and Berrow's Newspapers for the one on page 79; and apologises for any photographs used inadvertently without the owner's permission. John Kinsman, Stephen Saunders and Edwin John copied many of the prints for publication.

The plan on page 90 and the line drawings are the work of Charles Grant, while the maps have been prepared by Peter Russell.

The Society wishes to thank Birmingham University Extra Mural Group led by J. W. Tonkin, F.S.A., for permission to reproduce the plan drawn by Inett Homes on page 88, and Kay Bright and B. T. Batsford Ltd for their permission to print Geoffrey Bright's poem *Hops*.

Michael and Kay Carey, Charles Hopkinson and Colin Macdiarmid have read the manuscript with the eyes of those who previously knew little of hop growing, and have made many pertinent comments and helpful suggestions on how to present such diverse material.

Finally, Tony Hicks of Orphans Press Ltd has, once again, shown his expertise and customary patience in printing this the latest of the Society's publications.

Publication Committee

Philip Crosskey   *chairman*
Jean Hopkinson   *editor*
Daphne Davies
Lynda Duthy-James
Joan Leese
Suzanne Lowden
Ethel Paske
Harry Paske
Bill Rollason
Mildred Shepherd
Deborah Waller
Phyllis Williams

Introduction

Hops, hop growing. What on earth is a Local History Society doing in bringing out a book on this subject which is more in keeping with agriculture? One must have lived in a hop-growing area to understand the importance that this crop once had, not only for farmers but also for the community at large. There have been such rapid changes in both the agricultural and social fields in the last thirty years, that we felt it was important to provide some record of the excitement of hop picking before memories fade and pass into folklore.

The book naturally divides into two parts; the first deals with the social aspects of hop growing and hop picking, how it affected not only the local farmers and their wives and families, the farmworkers and the town, but also the hop pickers who came from the Black Country or South Wales in vast numbers. Some of the flavour of hop picking is reflected in the letters which we have received from those in the Black Country who were kind enough to respond to our appeal for information. Extracts from them will be found in later pages but hop picking certainly evoked poignant childhood memories, interludes from the grimness of the industrial areas.

But hops have to be grown before they can be picked and this is the concern of the second part of the book. A farmer who grows hops is busy all the year round in erecting and repairing wirework, cultivating, manuring, stringing, spraying, controlling the weeds and all the other jobs required to get a good harvest and good sample of hops.

A few acres of hops were grown on many mixed farms in the area and if one reads the diary of such a farmer there are few days in the course of twenty-seven years in which hops are not mentioned. But they were not the only crop; hay, corn, fruit, currants, stock rearing, poultry, etc., had all to be fitted in. In the 1950s there was a considerable labour force to do the work but as the years passed wages went up and the numbers employed went down, so that all activities had to be rationalized and machinery used instead of men and women.

Gradually the number of farmers who grow hops has decreased; the need for hops has diminished and competition from foreign hops has brought great pressure on the hop farmer to produce his crop as efficiently and economically as possible. But probably the biggest threat to the hop is a disease, verticillium wilt, for which there is no cure; although it has been the scourge of hop growing in Kent for some time, it has only recently affected the hopyards of Herefordshire.

We hope we have managed to marry the two interests of this book. It would be comparatively easy to produce a mainly photographic record with captions, using the prints from the Society's large collection, but we felt that we should try to produce some written record of wider interest with the help of local hop growers and put into perspective some of the many interesting facets of a crop which has engendered so much local history.

DANGER! VERTICILLIUM WILT!

Although we hope this book will stimulate curiosity about hops we must regrettably ask you not to enter a hopyard under any circumstances without the owner's permission.

Most roadside hopyards in Hereford and Worcester have signs asking you to keep out and some that have footpaths request you to take another route. This is solely because of the extreme danger of carrying and spreading the disease VERTICILLIUM WILT, a killer disease of hops for which unfortunately there is no cure. This disease has been rampant for many years in parts of Kent and has caused many people to give up hop growing.

Over twenty-eight farms in Hereford and Worcester have been infected since 1975 so farmers have good reason to be worried about the risk.

SO PLEASE KEEP OUT OF HOPYARDS.

CHAPTER 1

The Flavour in the Beer

'For Hops, we make haste to be the chief Hop-masters in *England;* our Country having store of Coppice-woods, and many provident men within these three yeares planting abundance of the fairest and largest sort of hops. All about *Bromyard* in a base (low-lying) soyle there is a great store.'

John Beale, 1656.

It is hard to imagine the disruption of normal commercial and social life that only a generation ago would descend on Bromyard and the surrounding countryside for a month each year. September meant one thing—hop picking.

Until the 16th century, England's national drink had been ale—a malted drink flavoured with alecost (costmary), alehoof (ground ivy), wormwood and other substances, but when hops were first used to flavour and preserve ale is unknown. There is evidence that they were cultivated in Bavaria in the 8th century, in the Low Countries in the 10th century, and 400 years later they were being imported into England. 'Strong ale' went out of fashion as the upper classes took to drinking imported wine, and the use of hops may have been encouraged by the need to find a way of flavouring and preserving the weaker 'small beer', which was made from inferior materials and which did not keep as well. 'Small beer' was cheap and therefore popular with the poor, and along with 'small cider' was used in part payment of servants and labourers. Hops were used to preserve 'small cider' made from a second pressing of the apples. Contrary to popular belief, the use of hops in brewing has no effect on the alcoholic content of beer. A dictionary published in London in 1440 gives as its definition of hops, 'sede for beyre', and Arnold's chronicle of 1502 records that beer was first made in London by 'beer brewers .... strangers, Flemings, Dutchmen', indicating that not only were the hops imported, but also the brewers.

It is often stated that an act was passed in 1424 banning the growth of hops, 'this wicked weed', as they were referred to. There is no evidence of this act in any form, although there certainly was opposition from herbalists and others on economic grounds. The plant has also been used to make coarse brown paper, strong sacking, binders for sheaves of corn, cinnamon-brown dye for wool, and as a substitute for oak bark in tanning.

The hop belongs to the same family as hemp and cannabis, and is a relative of the nettle. A hardy, long-lived, climbing perennial, its shoots can reach 20 feet in length but die back to ground level every winter. It has no tendrils and climbs clockwise round its support. Although it will grow in the poorest soils, only optimum conditions will produce the quality needed for today's shrinking markets. As a result, hop growing in Herefordshire is now concentrated in the sheltered river valleys of the Frome and Lugg, where there are at least 18 inches of loamy soil with a medium to heavy texture and a good structure for the roots to

Hops grown on poles and a load ready for drying at Brookhouse Farm, Avenbury, before the First World War. Elsie Cook, the booker, is standing next to her brother Hubert.

Hops ready for picking on wirework, the modern method of supporting the bines. Brewers use the hop cone with its bracts and glands containing various resins and oils.

establish permanent systems. A plentiful supply of water and food is needed for rapid growth and to balance the loss of moisture through the leaves, while good drainage is also essential to aerate the soil and prevent waterlogging. An unusually light rainfall averaging 12 inches between April and September, together with suitable temperatures, produce excellent oil and resin development in local hops. In some areas, the field in which they are grown is called a hop garden, however in Herefordshire it is always known as a hopyard.

By tradition, hops were first grown in England for beer in the 1520s in Kent. The practice soon spread to most other counties, including Herefordshire where the crop has been extensively cultivated in at least 80% of the county's parishes at some period during the last 400 years; in *A Tour Through Britain* published in 1724 Defoe observed that the inhabitants of Herefordshire were: 'a diligent and laborious people, chiefly addicted to husbandry and they boast, that they have the finest wool, the best hops, and the richest cyder, in all Britain .... As for hops they plant in abundance indeed all over the county, and they're very good.'

In the 16th and 17th centuries, hops were planted by inserting three plants, called stocks or setts, around the edges of large holes filled with rich fertile soil and located in rows across the hopyard. During the spring and summer, the surrounding ground was pared of weeds and built up round the setts to form a flat-topped conical mound called a hill. A long pole, usually of ash, chestnut or alder, was sunk in the ground at an angle by each sett so that it leant outwards, while two young shoots were trained up it and tied with a rush. All other shoots were removed from the sett. It was soon found that the weight of hops on the poles caused the wind to break or blow them over, and to help prevent this the poles were tied together at the top with strong twine. Until the discovery of wood preservatives such as creosote, the hop poles only lasted about two years. Thus, replacement of poles was a large, recurring expense, with up to 700 new poles per acre being needed each year, and this continuous demand was the main reason why there were so many ash beds and coppices in hop-growing districts. After the hops had been picked the ground between the hills was dug by hand and manured. A reference to hills occurs in a legal document dated 1638 for the manor of Buttas in King's Pyon, where there was a 'large new frame of buildings wherein there is a dairy house, a kiln house, a store house, six lofts well boarded for malting hop or other use' and a hopyard that 'hath 2000 hills furnished with 6000 poles'.

In the Bromyard district, the first reference to hops appears to be in Swithun Butterfield's survey of 1577 for the bishop of Hereford of the farms in Whitbourne: 'A lytle pcell of land called the hoppyarde lyeth between Brownyng land and Gregory Collins land, cont by estim. 1 rood.' By 1649 the 'hop-masters' of Bromyard had established the district as one of the main hop-growing areas of the country and the yards at Whitbourne Court 'though uncertain had been known to produce hops to the value of £700.' Hops are still grown at Poplands, Whitbourne, so they have been cultivated in the parish for well over 400 years.

Stephens' *Book of the Farm* lists: 'All the particulars requisite for the furnishing of a new hop ground and the expense per acre attending them is as follows:

	£	s.	d.
Draining	6	-	-
Spade and fork tending	7	-	-
Manure, 500 cubic yard at 3s.	7	10	-
Lime, 200 bushels @ 6d. and spreading	5	-	-
Harrowing and rolling		2	-
Setting off 1194 hills, at 6½ feet apart		2	-
Planting 1194 hills of bedded sets, @ 1/2 per 100		14	-
Compost for 1194 hills	1	-	-
3582 bedded plants at 6d. per 100		17	-
Twisting the young bines and repairing the hills in autumn		15	-
	£29	-	-

One man @ 3s., and assistant @ 2s., and 2 boys @ 6d. each, in all 6/-, will set off 3 acres a day. Two men @ 2s. each, and 1 boy @ 6d., in all 4/6 will plant 600 hills a day. In the first year of a new hopground, the soil between the hills may be cropped with a green crop, manured for itself, in order to keep the ground clean, and cause it to make some return for the great outlay incurred in converting it into a hop ground.'

By the end of the 18th century, hops were also being grown on long low ridges spaced six to eight feet apart, running from one side of the hopyard to the other, with the poles placed on the ridge and tied at the top with a string. Midway between the poles a vertical string often hung down from the top string, its lower end anchored into the ground with a special tool. After picking the poles were left in piles on the ground, later to be stacked in 'wigwams' for the winter. Creosote to preserve them became generally available in 1862 and many farms had their long narrow creosote tanks with a fireplace and chimney at one end. The creosote was heated to allow it to soak into the home-grown poles and fencing stakes, which were stood on end, whereas the poles for wirework were laid full length.

Loudon's *Encyclopaedia of Agriculture* of 1835 commented that: 'Wires of copper or iron have been tried as a substitute for wooden poles in the North of France .... we do not think it any improvement.' By the 1850s, nevertheless, because of the high cost of growing hops on poles and with wire already being used extensively for fencing, attempts were also being made in this country to grow hops on permanent wires similar to the espalier system used in fruit growing. This research led to the invention of hop wirework, a firmly anchored framework of posts and wires containing a network of strings reaching from each plant to the top wire up which the shoots could climb. By 1871 several of the larger growers in Herefordshire were using it. The patterns of wirework and stringing have varied from area to area, but all provide a system of wires and strings to support the crop, otherwise the whole row would collapse when the bine is pulled. Polework continued to be used in many smaller yards, for example at Lowdy Hall, Ullingswick, until 1958. Once a hopyard had been established, it would go on producing hops for fifteen years or more without replanting, provided it was properly cultivated and manured, and kept relatively free of disease. When a yard was nearing the end of its useful life, it was common practice to plant fruit trees in the hop rows. The trees were protected from grazing animals until the hops were removed about six

Winter work on a farm near Ledbury in 1934. Preparing new poles for the creosote tank.

Hop poles stacked in 'wigwams' for the winter at the Lays Farm, Tarrington.

years later, when the fruit trees would be large enough to need little protection. To this day, many orchards in the county still show the ridge and furrow of a hopyard with the trees growing on ridges.

In the early 19th century, no hop grower expected to pick a worthwhile crop more than one year in every three. This was because of the ravages of aphids (blight). Various attempts were made to control this damage, such as using smoke from bonfires, spreading foul-smelling dung, and hanging sticky flypapers. Towards the end of the century, it was discovered that a mixture of boiled soft soap and quassia mixed with water and sprayed onto the hop plant would reduce the infestation. This is one of the reasons why at many farmsteads one finds in the back kitchen or amongst the farm buildings very large washboilers or furnaces used to prepare the spray. On the larger hop farms central steam-driven pumping stations were established, the spray being boiled by steam and then pumped through pipes to tanks in the hopyards used to fill the sprayers. The small growers used hand-pumped sprayers or knapsack sprayers, while the larger growers had heavy power sprayers pulled by three horses with the pump being driven from the wheels.

So far, twenty references to hops have been found in the county's wills and inventories up to 1700, and two extracts show the changes in hop-picking techniques that were taking place. The early method of picking hops in Herefordshire was to spread a picking sheet, a blanket or a hessian sheet, on the ground and to pick the hops on to it. Picking sheets are often listed in inventories in the Bromyard district up to the late 17th century, but unlike other areas never picking baskets. From 1700 onwards there are increasing mentions of hop cribs and crib cloths. The first inventory is dated 9 October 1682 and is that of John Norgroves of 'Witbourne', yeoman:

'Hops in the house	6 lb		
One old kiln hair, one old sack, one picking sheet, two			
old bags and two pairs of scales	£3	6s	8d
400 hop poles	4s		
Hop poles in Richard Lovedale's house	£1'		

Norgroves used a sheet, but a decade later the second inventory of 23 March 1692 shows that William Toombs of Pencombe, blacksmith, had been picking his hops into a crib:

'A small parcel of hops and a stone of wool	14s	8d
6 Bushels of Lent grain, one old hair cloth, a crib cloth		
and scales	13s'	

When Thomas Lane of Tipton Hall, Tedstone Delamere, died in 1732, the inventory indicated that he had been making both beer and cider:

'In the Servantemens Room two bedds and a todd of			
old hopps	£ 2	0s	0d
In the Back Kitchen two ffurnaces & other Lumber	£ 2	10s	0d
In the Killhouse two Killhares & One maltmill two			
Grates and other things there	£ 2	0s	0d
The Cydermill Screws Hares and all appurtenances			
thereto	£ 3	10s	0d
Hogsheads Tubbs Sceels Coopers ware together with			
the Cider & malt Drink in them	£13	0s	0d'

The same year Matthew God of Westwood, Thornbury, dried his crop in a kiln using charcoal, and Herbert Osborn of Stoke Prior died leaving 'In the Brew House a small Brass furnace & Irons & Iron Boiler'.

The cribs, called bins in Kent, were rough wooden frames about 7 feet by 3 feet with hessian sewn on to form containers, and in 1774, Thomas Lewis, maltster, in the Butcher Row, Hereford, (of which only the Old House remains) was advertising 'A quantity of HOP-SACKING of the best sorts'. The men employed as polepullers moved the cribs up the rows, which were divided into 'houses' to regulate the picking in the yards. The walls of each house were formed by two adjacent rows, and in polework the length consisted of about twenty stocks, while in wirework the crosswires defined the length. In each case all bines within the house had to be picked before the crib was moved into the next one. In polework, the poles were pulled out of the ground and rested on the end of the crib and the bines, which had twisted round and round the poles, had to be cut off before the actual picking could start. In wirework, the bines were cut off about 4 feet above ground and then pulled off the top wire, and dropped into the crib for picking. If a farm had both wirework and polework, the pole hops were often picked at a higher price than the wirework ones as they were disliked by the pickers. Also unpopular were the bad patches of hops into which the farmer's children and their friends often found the house crib moved, lest the regular pickers should feel 'hard done by' and a surprising slowness come upon them at the approach of the offending patch!

The early pickers were the farm labourers' wives and children, and at Hanley, Worcestershire, in 1753, the rate for three weeks work for a woman was 9s. 6d. By 1840 piece-work was being advocated at which a good picker could earn 1s. 6d. a day. With the coming of the railways it became popular to import labour from South Wales or the Black Country, attracted not only by the prospect of hop picking but by the chance to stock up with apples for the winter. They came to the nearest railway station in special trains, as many as 2,000 or more arriving in a day at small country stations. Until the opening of the Bromyard line in the 1870s, the Black Country pickers for Whitbourne, Knightwick and Suckley travelled by train as far as Stourport, then made their way to the big yard at the Dog Inn at Dunley and from there were taken by horse drawn wagons to the surrounding farms, often involving long journeys with pickers, children, dogs, luggage, cooking utensils, all piled in together. They were housed in farm buildings, tents, or in flimsy hovels known as barracks. This may be one of the reasons why some hop farms appear to have more buildings with lofts than other farms, these extra so-called tallets having been originally floored as a way of using roof space to house hop pickers.

After arriving by train, pickers loading on to a wagon to go to the farm.

Picking polework at Lower Court, Ullingswick, in 1902. Four cribs abreast in their 'houses', with poles resting on the two nearest cribs ready for picking.

Bushelling at Avenbury Court in 1905 - the boy is waiting to mark the tally stick. A bushel, in this case a basket, is a measure of capacity equal to 8 gallons (36 litres) also used for corn and fruit.

After the hops had been picked into the crib they had to be measured or bushelled. The busheller called out the count in a loud voice as he measured the green (freshly picked) hops into a sack held by the sack holder. The count was kept by a tally man who carried a quantity of tallies hung on a belt. These were pieces of wood about 15 inches long, split into two pieces, the second piece of the pair being given to the picker. The two pieces would only fit together in a certain position and the count was recorded by file marks across both pieces. By the late 19th century, Herefordshire growers were using hop checks or tokens which were coin-like discs of brass, iron or zinc, of several sizes, stamped with the grower's name. The smallest represented single bushels which were exchanged for others marked 1, 3, 5, 10 and £1, indicating the amount earned in shillings and pounds. These were counted out to the picker at each bushelling and exchanged for cash at the end of picking. They were later replaced by the booking system. The booker entered the amount in his or her book and in a smaller book retained by the picker. In the evenings there would always be pickers wanting a 'sub' or part-payment for their work. This would entail the return of the checks or it would have to be entered in both the picker's and the master's books, care being taken that the grower always owed the picker some money, otherwise the picker might leave. The rate paid per bushel was agreed between growers and pickers, usually after the first day's picking, and in the 1920s and '30s varied between about 5 bushels to the shilling if hops were big and in good condition, and 2 bushels to the shilling for those that were very small or diseased.

For at least 300 years Herefordshire has grown more hops than the local brewers needed. As Defoe noted in 1724, cider was 'the common drink of the county, and so very good and cheap, that we never found fault, though we could get no other drink for 20 miles together.' Thus few of the hops rushed to the Annual Hop Fairs at Worcester on September 19th and to the Hereford fairs for 'cattle, cheese, hops and linen', are likely to have been for local consumption. Notoriously bad roads, the Wye only navigable with difficulty, no canal until 1845 and no railway until 1853, would have added considerably to the cost of transport, but this was offset to some extent by the fact that the crop could be produced more cheaply in Herefordshire than in other parts of the country. The demand was there, however, helped by government propaganda in favour of beer drinking instead of gin. With the expansion of the towns, breweries were established all over the country, and some years a million barrels of beer were produced in London and the suburbs alone. Between 1880 and the 1920s, Ledbury, Leominster and Tenbury each had several small breweries registered, although Bromyard appears to have had none. Many farmers secured their markets by direct contracts with West Midland brewers who preferred the high quality, less coarse varieties grown locally. One such grower was Perry Pudge of New House, Bishops Frome, who took pockets of hops, known as 'Pudges', to the Black Country before the First World War and sold them individually to small breweries there.

There are numerous references to hops in the *Hereford Journal*. For instance, in October 1770: 'At our fair, on Saturday last, hops sold from £4. 4s. to £6 .... And on Monday hops advanced considerably.' The same month storage space was being offered: 'HOPS may stand, on very reasonable Terms, in a large and commodious Room, which will be always ready for their Reception during the Season, at the Red-Streak-Tree Inn, in this City.' In November a Mr George inadvertently found himself providing unplanned warehouseroom: *'WHEREAS* at *HEREFORD FAIR* on Saturday the 20th inst. a *POCKET* of *HOPS* was sent away, by Mistake, with other Hops, the Property of Mr Philip George of Worcester: Whoever can prove it to be their Property (by applying to Mr George) may have it again, paying for Costs and Charges.' Then on 17 September 1851 there was an appeal that:

> 'Whenever we have a railway into this city, immediate steps must be taken for establishing a hop market, here, in order that the farmers may dispose of Hereford hops in their own county, and not have the trouble of journeying to a distant market to sell what may be disposed of at their own doors—great part of the hops of Herefordshire being disposed of at Worcester, acquire the title of "Worcester hops" and thus rob us of the celebrity of our own county's growth.'

Six years later the plea had been partially heeded with the building of the Corn Exchange in Broad Street where the corn merchants also held a hop market, and in season the smell of hops permeated Broad Street from a hop warehouse next to the Exchange. Although the first railway lines had reached Hereford in 1853, *Slater's Directory* of 1859 states that cider, grain, hops and oak bark were still being 'conveyed down the Wye, and by the canal to Gloucester and other places.' The

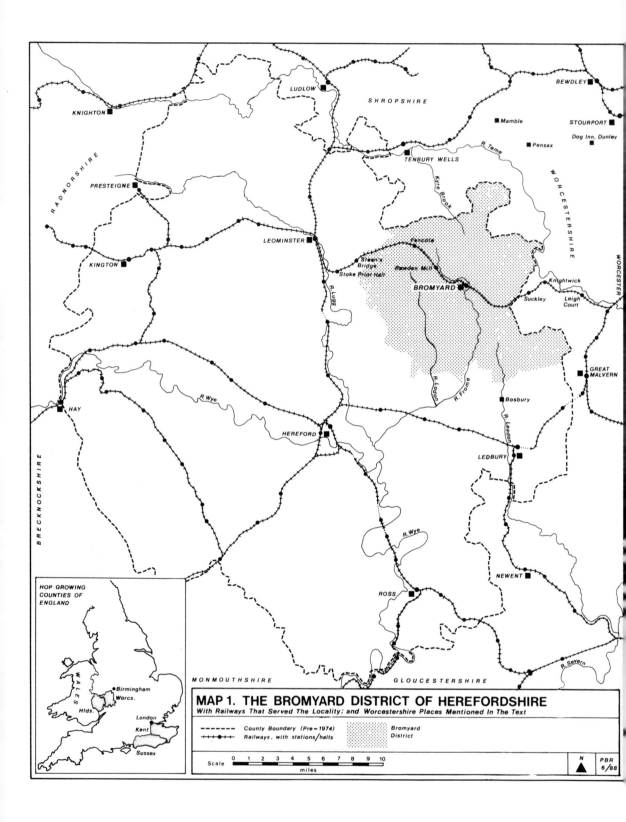

KNIGHTON

RADNORSHIRE

PRESTEIGNE

KINGTON

LUDLOW

SHROPSHIRE

Mamble

Pensax

BEWDLEY

STOURPORT

Dog Inn, Dunley

TENBURY WELLS

R. Teme

Kyre Brook

WORCESTERSHIRE

WORCESTER

LEOMINSTER

Fencote

Steen's Bridge

Stoke Prior Halt

Rowden Mill

BROMYARD

R. Lugg

Knightwick

Suckley

Leigh Court

BRECKNOCKSHIRE

R. Wye

HAY

HEREFORD

R. Frome

R. Loden

Bosbury

R. Leadon

GREAT MALVERN

LEDBURY

R. Wye

ROSS

NEWENT

R. Severn

MONMOUTHSHIRE

GLOUCESTERSHIRE

HOP GROWING COUNTIES OF ENGLAND

WALES

Birmingham

Worcs.

Hfds.

London

Kent

Sussex

MAP 1. THE BROMYARD DISTRICT OF HEREFORDSHIRE

With Railways That Served The Locality; and Worcestershire Places Mentioned In The Text

- - - - County Boundary (Pre–1974)
+•+•+ Railways, with stations/halts

Bromyard District

Scale 0 1 2 3 4 5 6 7 8 9 10
miles

N

PBR
6/88

next year the Worcester/Hereford line was opened and barge traffic began to decline. The Corn Exchange was converted into the Kemble Theatre in 1911, but it continued to be used as a corn exchange on Wednesdays when there would be no matinées. The theatre had a sliding roof which could be opened on hot summer nights and to clear the atmosphere between performances. The corn exchange ceased operating in 1950 and the theatre was demolished in 1963. There were other markets such as those at Chelmsford and Salisbury, but the largest was the Borough Market in London, and when the telephone exchange for the Borough High Street was built it was called Hopmarket.

Home brewing of beer would have created a need for small quantities of hops. A household guide of *c*1800, *The Young Woman's Companion or Female Instructor,* assured its readers that an excellent table beer fit for drinking in three or four weeks could be made from 3 bushels of malt, yeast, 39 gallons of water and 1½ pounds of hops. During the Napoleonic wars, however, the rise in the price of malting barley and hops made home brewing too expensive for poorer households and beer was largely replaced by tea in the home, with a visit to the public house for any beer drinking. In 1851 four innkeepers in Bromyard were still doing their own brewing and malting. The practice which had started in the 18th century of farmers paying their labourers' wages partly in beer or cider, was understandably frowned on by the Temperance Movement, and home-brewed beer rapidly disappeared from farmhouses after 1880 when a duty was imposed on beer. The Truck Acts of 1887 and 1896 made the daily cider allowance in lieu of wages illegal, but it was so popular with their labourers that it was continued by many local farmers as a free issue.

Hops have always proved an erratic source of income. Disease, pests, taxes and the weather made fluctuations in yields and profits such a regular feature of the 18th century that betting on the rate of hop duty was a popular pastime at Worcester market. The first half of the 19th century saw the highest acreage of hops ever planted in the Bromyard district with 4,251 acres in 1835, but over-production, blight and foreign competition, led to a drop of 65% by 1860. A gradual rise then occurred until, in 1900, the figure was back to 2,050 acres, about half the peak acreage of 1835. By the First World War, foreign dumping had caused a drop of 45%, since when there has been a slow but steady contraction to about 650 acres in 1985 (see graph on page 161).

Eighteenth-century writers also depict the uncertain nature of hop growing. In 1729, Richard Bradley, a professor of botany at Cambridge, wrote that ground previously worth less than a shilling an acre, was now fetching up to £50 a year if planted with hops. By 1793, however, Nathaniel Kent, who knew the Tenbury district well, was complaining in his *Hints to Gentlemen of Landed Property* that hop growing in Hereford and Worcester was not in the long-term interests of landowners, as tenants were keeping most of the farmyard manure for their hops and sacrificing good pasture for alder beds to supply hop poles. Fifteen years later, *The Leominster Guide* while remarking on the size of the local hop grounds and how some farmers had managed to buy the farms they had previously rented, continued that great profits no longer existed owing to overproduction, heavy duties, and the brewers finding substitutes.

The hopyard at Lower Court, Ullingswick, again. There is a wealth of detail in this photograph with the poles, a milk can and lunch baskets in the shade of the rigid Herefordshire crib, the large old kitchen knife stuck in the corner post, the sacking aprons and the cotton sun bonnets. A small brother minds the toddler whilst his older sisters help their mother pick.

Ale, beer and hops had long been targets for taxation; the last item in the Domesday list of Herefordshire customs records that, 'Any man's wife who brewed ale inside or outside the City gave 10d as a customary due.' As with all agricultural produce since earliest times, farmers paid tithe on their hops and in 1835 Loudon explained that: 'When tythe of hops is taken in kind the parson may either take every tenth basket when green or every tenth sack when dried in the latter case allowing 25s. per cwt for drying, sacking and duty.' A good source of information on hop growing that can be used in any county are the tithe maps and apportionments prepared as a result of the Tithe Commutation Act of 1836. This abolished the payment of tithe in kind, where it still existed, and substituted a money rent instead. As hops were assessed separately, it is possible to discover which farmers were growing them in which fields. For example, in 1841 a third of all the farms and smallholdings in Little Cowarne had a hopyard however small; of the 693 acres in the parish 50 acres were devoted to hops. A year later in the adjacent parish of Stoke Lacy (2,584 acres), just over a quarter of the 88 farms and smallholdings had hopyards ranging in size from ½-6½ acres, with three-quarters of the crop being produced on the 7 largest farms. Field names, such as the Old Hop Yard, often indicate farms which had grown hops in the past, but were no longer doing so by the date of the apportionment; evidence of hop growing has been found in 207 of the 250 or so parishes of Herefordshire.

In addition to tithe, hop farmers paid an excise duty, and 1711 saw the introduction of hop duty. The excise list at the British Library for the years 1807-1861 shows that for many years Herefordshire was growing over 10,000 acres or nearly a quarter of the total crop. The excise officers had to be notified when picking was due to start, so that they could supervise the drying, weighing and packing of the hops, and on 3 September 1851 the *Hereford Journal* reported that, 'The excisemen have commenced their rounds.'

Two seasons of low prices in 1821 and 1822 had caused hardship, and an urn was presented to John Walker, the great-great-great-grandfather of Peter Walker of Ankerdine, Knightwick, for his 'unwearied exertions in assisting to obtain a remission of part of the Hop Duty for the year 1822'; and in 1849 a deputation to the chancellor of the exchequer tried to delay the collection of the duty due in October. A further deputation from all the hop growing districts in March 1862 urged the chancellor to abolish both hop duty and excise duty and later that year they were repealed. The same year import duty was removed, but in spite of foreign competition the national acreage planted increased until 1878 when it was 71,789 acres, the highest recorded.

Four years later there was a devastating attack of aphids, and the total yield dropped from the 455,000 cwt of 1881 to only 120,000 cwt, and the price of hops increased threefold from approximately £5 to £15 per cwt. Only four years on again, in 1886, there was a bumper crop when extra accommodation had to be found for the pockets of hops in Worcester at the Skating Rink, the old Exhibition Building, the Guildhall and the Shirehall. In the last decade of the century, while the national acreage was declining, the acreage in the Bromyard district actually continued to increase. An increase also occurred in Worcestershire, mainly in the Teme Valley, and this mirrors the local trend where it was the farmers on the better ground in the parishes of Avenbury, Bishops Frome, Bromyard, Cradley,

A group of pickers and visitors at Thornbury Court in 1914.

Much Cowarne and Whitbourne, who were increasing their acreages, while the acreages in the more upland parishes continued to decline. Additional factors that contributed to the success of those who managed to stay in hop farming and expand, were the readiness of the Herefordshire and Worcestershire growers to adopt new methods such as wirework and the use of horse-drawn ploughs in the yards, unlike their more conservative counterparts in the south, and also their direct contracts with West Midland brewers.

By 1905 the picture was not so satisfactory and on 7 September the *Bromyard News and Record* reported that, in his evidence to the Agricultural Committee of the Tariff Commission, the well-known hop factor, Mr Edward Le May, brought out clearly the economic advantages to this country that would flow from a revival of the hop industry, which had declined in acreage by a third since 1878. A week later, the paper returned to the subject of hops:

> 'The wet weather must have been of great discomfort to pickers, for nearly every day in the past fortnight it has rained, and at times very heavily too. Prices offered for good samples the last two Saturdays have been very disheartening and many a grower came back last week with the determination of having "no more". There is not much prospect of prices improving either, especially when the foreign berries arrive in England—free of duty.'

The industry was in a depressed state and numerous meetings were held to protest against the dumping of foreign hops and to campaign for an import duty. Imports had been building up since the 1850s, and by 1900 had reached as many as 150,000 cwt from the U.S.A., 35,000 cwt from Belgium and 12,000 cwt from Germany. (The present market share for growers, it is hoped, is about 120,000 cwt, excluding imports and even brewer-growers.) T. Lawson Walker of Knightwick Manor helped organise a mass meeting of growers and pickers in London on 16 May 1908, Hop Saturday, and he was one of the speakers at the meeting in Trafalgar Square. *Berrow's Worcester Journal* described how:

> 'Early in the day local growers, accompanied by bands of labourers, wended their way to the various stations on the Hereford and Leominster lines to join the special trains. Nearly 400 travelled by the special on the Leominster line and 500 to 600 by the Hereford train. The two contingents met at Shrub Hill. Those travelling from the Tenbury district, together with a large company of pickers from the Black Country proceeded via Birmingham and Oxford. Local growers took numbers of their own men with them and paid their fares ... More than 50,000 marched in procession to Trafalgar Square.'

It was said that many Herefordshire growers, with those from other areas, did not get any further than the first pub near Paddington Station! They did at least have a good day out, but the government of the day took no action to improve the situation and by 1914 the pressure of continuing imports caused a further national decline of over 2,000 acres.

This account of aspects of hop growing prior to the First World War sets the scene for the earliest photographs and recollections, while the developments in the industry that have since taken place can be found in chapters 9-12.

Soldiers from Frome Bank Convalescent Home, Bromyard, picking at Little Froome during the First World War.

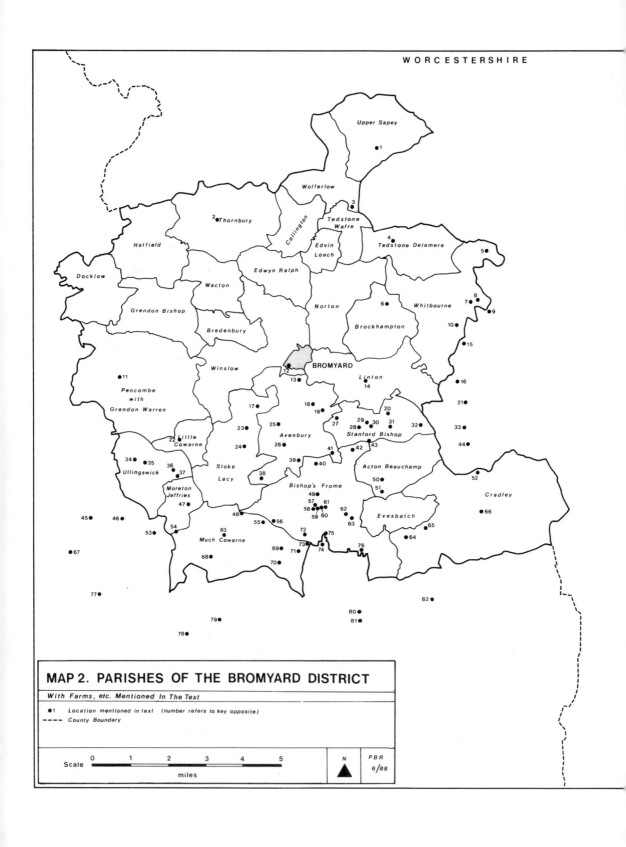

WORCESTERSHIRE

Upper Sapey

●1

Wolferlow

●3

2●Thornbury

Collington

Tedstone
Wafre

Edvin
Loach

4●
Tedstone Delamere

5●

Hatfield

Edwyn Ralph

8●
7●
9●

Docklow

Wacton

Norton

6●

Whitbourne

10●

Grendon Bishop

Bredenbury

Brockhampton

15●

BROMYARD

●12

Winslow

13●

Linton
14

16●

●11

17●

18●
19●

20●

21●

Pencombe
with
Grendon Warren

23●

25●

29●
28●
27●

30●
31●

32●

33●

22●Little
Cowarne

24●

Avenbury

26●

Stanford Bishop

34● ●35

39●

41●

42● 43

44●

36●

●40

Ullingswick

37●

Stoke

Acton Beauchamp

Moreton
Jeffries

Lacy

38●

50●

52●

47●

48●

Bishop's Frome

49●

51●

Cradley

45●   46●

54●

55● ●56

57●
58● 61
59● 60

62●

Evesbatch

66●

53●

83●
Much Cowarne

72●

63●

65●

●67

68●

69●

73●

75●
74●

76●

64●

71●

70●

77●

82●

80●

79●

81●

78●

MAP 2. PARISHES OF THE BROMYARD DISTRICT

With Farms, etc. Mentioned In The Text

●1   Location mentioned in text (number refers to key opposite)
----   County Boundary

Scale   0   1   2   3   4   5
              miles

N

PBR
6/88

Key to Map 2

Name	No	Name	No
Ankerdine Farm, Doddenham	9	Little Cowarne Court, Little Cowarne	22
Avenbury Court, Avenbury	18	Little Froome, Avenbury	13
The Baiting House, Upper Sapey	1	Lowdy Hall, Ullingswick	35
The Bean House, Cradley	66	Lower Court, Suckley	33
Bromtrees Hall, Bishops Frome	56	Lower Court, Ullingswick	36
Brookhouse Farm, Avenbury	19	Lower Hope, Ullingswick	34
The Bull Ring, Stanford Bishop	30	Lower House, Stanford Bishop	28
Burley Gate Shop and P.O., Much Cowarne	54	Lower Tedney, Whitbourne	5
The Chase Inn, Bishops Frome	60	Lower Town, Preston Wynne	67
Church House, Pencombe	11	The Major's Arms, Bishops Frome	63
The Court, Bishops Frome (demolished)	61	Mayfields Farm, Bishops Frome	62
Cowarne Court, Much Cowarne	68	Merryfield Farm, Stoke Lacy	24
Cradley Hall Farm, Cradley	64	Mintridge, Stoke Lacy	17
Dovehills, Bishops Frome	42	Monksbury Court, Yarkhill	79
The Farm, Brockhampton	6	Moorend, Much Cowarne	69
The Farm, Moreton Jeffries	47	Munderfield Court, Avenbury	26
Felton Court, Felton	46	Nashend Farm, Bosbury	82
The Fir Tree Inn, Much Cowarne	71	The New House, Bishops Frome	75
The Five Bridges Inn, Much Cowarne	73	Newton Farm, Stoke Lacy	23
Frogend Farm, Castle Frome	74	Panks Bridge Farm, Much Cowarne	48
Fromes Hill, Bishops Frome	76	Pauncefort Court, Much Cowarne	83
Garford, Yarkhill	78	Pewcroft, Suckley	16
Gold Hill, Bosbury	81	Poplands, Whitbourne	7
The Green Dragon Inn, Bishops Frome	59	Rosemaund E.H.F., Felton	45
The Hawkins, Stanford Bishop	29	Searchlight Post, Bromyard	12
The Heath, Avenbury	25	The Seed, Cradley	65
The Herefordshire House, Stanford Bishop	20	Sevington, Acton Beauchamp	50
High Lane, Wolferlow/Tedstone Del/Wafre	3	Stanford Court, Stanford Bishop	31
Hill Farm, Bosbury	80	The Stocks, Suckley	44
Hillhampton, Ocle Pychard	53	Summerpool Hill, Bishops Frome	49
The Holly Bush Inn, Avenbury	39	Thinghill Court, Withington	77
Hope House, Stanford Bishop	32	Thornbury Court, Thornbury	2
Hope's Rough, Much Cowarne	55	The Three Crowns Inn, Ullingswick	37
Hopton, Stoke Lacy	38	Tin Town, Bishops Frome	58
Huntlands, Whitbourne	10	Tipton Hall, Tedstone Delamere	4
The Hyde, Stanford Bishop	27	Upper House, Bishops Frome	57
Instone Court, Bishops Frome	40	The Venn, Avenbury	41
Jumpers Hole, Stanford Bishop	43	Walton, Bishops Frome	72
Kidley, Acton Beauchamp	51	Whitbourne Court, Whitbourne	8
Knightwick Manor, Knightwick	15	The White House, Suckley	21
Leighton Court, Much Cowarne	70	Winthill Farm, Cradley	52
Linton Brook, Linton	14		

CHAPTER 2

A View from the Farmhouse

'Whome fancie persuadeth, among other crops,
to have for his spending, sufficient of hops ....'

Thomas Tusser, 1524?-1580.

During hop picking the usual pattern of life was disturbed for the whole area. Bromyard became a ghost town with nothing stirring—except on a Saturday afternoon. No public functions were held and nothing could be done until 'after hop picking'. Hop farmers and their families remained at home except for essential business and shopping, and meals were fitted in to suit bushelling and kiln changes.

At the turn of the century, the Eckleys lived at Church House, Pencombe, where the hops were grown up poles, and Mrs Eckley, who was more interested in the crop than her husband was, did the tying before the birth of her daughter in 1899. When they moved to Munderfield Court, Avenbury, there were local pickers and others from Dudley; on arrival the latter, taking their own plates, collected a hot meal of roast beef and vegetables from the farmhouse. Their sleeping quarters were over the cowshed with a kitchen nearby in a wainhouse where there was a fireplace for cooking. The one man among the pickers had his own 'bedroom' curtained off at the end of the sleeping quarters and he went to bed first.

In the evenings the pickers entertained themselves. They were all great dancers; one of them, Sarah Anne, who was also a good singer, did the cakewalk to the delight of the Eckley children. In contrast, knowing Mr Eckley was considered a religious man, there was nightly hymn-singing ending with the pickers standing outside the farmhouse to sing, 'Lead, Kindly Light'. Many of the women sold their crochet work locally. When the pickers went home, the boxes of provisions they had brought with them were full of apples and other fruits to which they had helped themselves. At Christmas Mrs Eckley always sent a turkey to Dudley for her pickers.

Of all the local villages, it was Bishops Frome which saw the greatest influx of pickers and a whole town would develop there. In the years before the First World War and during the '20s and '30s, the population of about 700 increased to 5,000 or more, largely because of the hop-growing empire built up by William Farmer Pudge born at New House, Bishops Frome, in 1851. Pudges had long been connected with Bishops Frome, but it was Farmer Pudge, a shrewd businessman, who turned from running the Chase Inn and a butcher's shop to concentrate on hops, and in the 1880s and 1890s bought Upper House, Walton and the Court specifically for the purpose. During the First World War he grew wheat, but planted up with hops again when peace returned. Between the Wars, he was said to be the largest private hop grower in England with over 200 acres of hops in

Hop picking at Munderfield Court in 1909, *L. to r.* Three Dudley pickers, Edith Passey, Kate Eckley, William Ingram (polepuller), Mrs. Ingram, Annie Vernalls, William Nottingham (polepuller), and a Dudley picker. *In front* ? and Jimmy Eckley.

Bishops Frome, together with many other hop farms in the area. 'It was just like looking at a sea of hops off the top of Fromes Hill,' says Gilbert Hyde. Busloads came on outings from Wales to walk the yards just before picking, and Pudge is reputed to have offered a shilling to anyone who could find a weed. When asked what he put on his hops, he would only divulge that it was 'the best, the best!' After a fire which gutted the hop kilns at the Court in 1926, he salvaged the red bricks from the service quarters at Cowarne Court and built a massive new drying complex at Upper House, behind the Chase Inn, with twelve 20 foot kilns under one roof, the largest in the country.

Farmer Pudge died in 1938 and his only daughter, Mrs Woodward, continued the business until it was wound up about 1962, when the drying complex behind the Chase Inn was relegated to a warehouse. These buildings have now been demolished to make way for houses, but Pudges are still growing hops at the New House, Frogend, Moorend and Bromtrees Hall.

A peaceful view of the Chase Inn, Bishops Frome, about 1910, with the Green Dragon in the background.

BISHOPS FROOME.

THE NEW KILN COMPLEX AT
UPPER HOUSE, BISHOPS FROME,
IN 1927.

Unloading sacks on to the greenstage.

Farmer Pudge.

The press in the hop room with kiln hairs
full of hops waiting to be bagged in the background.

Gypsy encampment with cooking pots hung over the fire.

Pudge imported all his pickers. Those from South Wales were accommodated on Upper House Farm in various sheds and barracks known as 'Tin Town'; while in fields on the back road to Burley Gate near the Filly Brook, there would be row upon row of caravans. In one field those belonging to the gypsies, the real Romanies, and in another, those of the didicoys or 'hedgecrawlers' (a Herefordshire word for tinkers). Gilbert Bowler remembers: 'It was a grand sight to see the gypsies arriving in their caravans with the dogs tied to the back axles, and horses and foals running behind.' And Edith Silcock knew them as 'tidy, respectable people who did not mix much with the other pickers. They might snare a few rabbits, but they were an honest lot, the troublemakers "coming from away". If any of the gypsy girls, and they were very pretty, strayed from their cribs one of their men-folk soon rounded them up and brought them back. They always had a number of horses and ponies with them, and on Sundays horse dealing would go on outside the Chase Inn, the men running up and down the road to show off the good points of their animals.' Wads of money were seen to change hands, always going to the head of the family. Every year a butcher from the Butter Market in Hereford used to set up a stall in Bishops Frome and he is still remembered for his call, 'If you wants to buy some meat, buy some meat, if not move the baby's ass off the slab!' The *Bromyard News and Record* of 1 October 1931 carried an end of season report: 'Round Bishops Frome the yards are denuded, but in "camp town" near the Roman Catholic Church there are still many residents, the children of whom—of which there were many without stockings or boots—seem to hop about most cheerfully in spite of the thorns and brambles.'

Hops had been grown for many years at Instone Court, Bishops Frome, when the farm was bought in 1920 by Sidney Parker; his family had been hop growers for many generations and there are still five Parkers in the area maintaining the tradition. At Instone cartsheds and wainhouses were used as eating places for the imported pickers. Planks and doors placed on empty drums served as tables and although benches were provided some preferred to sit on large blocks of wood. Each family had an allotted space arranged by the ganger woman and most had pieces of American oil cloth or newspaper for a tablecloth. For sleeping, haylofts, pigsties, cattle pens, etc, were cleaned up and partitions made for families by hanging hessian from the beams to meet the low wooden divisions of the range of pigsties. Boltings of straw were used to make beds. Blankets and hessian sheets were issued on the day of arrival, to be returned on leaving and all were washed as soon as possible afterwards. At the beginning of the next season they were put on the kilns for airing and this also served as a trial run for the kilns themselves. Premises had to be whitewashed and seen by the Sanitary Inspector before they were occupied, and latrines provided.

Sidney Parker.

Instone Court with its hop kilns and other farm buildings.

Fires were a frequent hazard on hop farms and must have been grim with no telephones and only horse drawn fire engines. Sidney Parker, who had a horror of fire after experiencing one started by a hurricane lamp in a cowshed, would only allow one coke devil for cooking; however, his pickers also had the use of open fires with properly built chimneys, faggots made up during the winter providing the fuel. Before electricity, hurricane lamps were used—dozens of them. Each morning they were brought up to the house for refilling, the job of the unfortunate 'boy'. Farms in the area were not connected to mains electricity until after the Second World War; however many generated their own supply by installing a dynamo and making use of the stationary engine which was used to drive the fan for the hop kilns. The house at Instone Court was wired for lighting during the 1920s, but with only 50v direct current its use was very limited. In the '30s, a set of storage batteries was obtained which gave greater scope and no time was lost in wiring the hop pickers' quarters—for safety reasons as much as anything else. After the Second World War ex-Army equipment proved very suitable. A large Nissen hut with a cast iron cooker and folding tables and benches were used for the dining room, and other Nissen huts with brick partitions were occupied as sleeping quarters.

Tramps just turned up at Instone, often pushing a pram containing their worldly possessions. They moved from one workhouse to another, occasionally taking on casual work, and were known as 'Milestone Inspectors'. They had to be housed separately from the other pickers and led a very private life of their own. They were not usually very good pickers but managed to earn some money during the season which helped them on their way. They used to lodge small sums with the landlord of the Holly Bush for future use.

On arrival at Cradley Hall Farm, the Dudley pickers were provided with tea and buns by Ethel Paske: 'The tea made in the coal-fired copper in which I did my family washing—I wonder now how I got rid of the taste of soap!' At Instone, a milk churn full of tea was taken down from the house in a donkey cart for breakfast in the hopyard at 9 a.m., and at the first measuring faggots were provided for the pickers to make fires to boil their kettles. The last measuring was usually about 5 p.m. The Parkers ran a shop at the house which sold eggs, butter and home-made cakes when available, rabbits caught on the farm 6d each, and skim milk at 1d a pint. Containers for the milk varied—billycans, jugs, and bottles which were almost impossible to keep clean and which smelt worse and worse as the season progressed. The waste was terrible, particularly bread, and kept the pigs going throughout hop picking with very little extra feeding.

The farmer's wife looked after not only the pickers, but also the key men of the harvest, the driers, with their twenty-four hour job. At Little Froome three men worked in the kilns, and they were provided with four meat meals a day and a middle night feed of meat, pickles, butter, cheese and so on. At Instone Court the driers ate in the house for breakfast, dinner, tea and supper, and were supplied with sandwiches and tea-making equipment for the night. On one occasion instead of sugar in a honey jar, Epsom salts in a similar jar were sent in by mistake with a disastrous effect on the driers as they had been adding more and more in a vain attempt to sweeten their tea!

With the war came food rationing, making more work for the farmer's wife and family; the pickers, imported and local, were entitled to extra rations at agricultural rates. 'This was a great thing and a lump of cheese doled out into one's crib on Monday morning was borne home later in triumph, for the ordinary weekly cheese ration was not more than 2 oz,' remembers Mildred Shepherd. On outlying farms away from shops, such as Knightwick Manor and Lower Tedney, the government allowed groceries to be delivered in bulk and the farmers' wives had to weigh up the rations for the pickers—a gargantuan task. At Little Froome, however, Ethel Paske's grocer was very good about doing up and delivering the small portions of butter or margarine, sugar, cheese, tea and jam, for the 150 or so local pickers. Each week they came up to the house for the rations and she took the money. The same thing happened at Instone Court where the ration books of the imported pickers were handed to the grocers. The pickers wrote their orders and Burtons put them up to be distributed by the farm shop, likewise the butcher. Bread was delivered three times a week but pickers did not like it after the first day; however, if it was warmed up in the Aga they were happy. One picker lived next door to a bakery and was used to new bread for every meal.

The declaration of war in 1939 had made many of the pickers from South Wales and the Black Country afraid to leave their homes, fearing they would be bombed. So there was a shortage of pickers and the picking dragged on into

Edith Silcock booking at Perry Pudge's, The New House, Bishops Frome, in 1939. Corporal Wells and other Bromyard Territorials were drafted in to help with the crop when there was a shortage of regular pickers.

October. To help out, some of the men and N.C.O.s of the local company of the Territorial Army were sent along each day but, as may be imagined, they regarded this as a pleasant holiday and not many hops got picked. The same season, preparatory to the issue of Identity Cards, a list had to be compiled of the dates of birth and full names of all the imported pickers and their children, many of whom were very vague about these details. Later on in the war, there was a cosmopolitan crowd on a farm at Burley Gate with two German prisoners of war, and one side of the farm for English people and the other side for the Welsh. On Saturday nights they all sang and the Welsh and the prisoners played accordions.

September 1944 at Lower Court, Ullingswick. *L. to r.* Tom Hamer, Frank Hall, Gwen Brookes, Pini Antonia, Biagio Chibelli, Antonio Bassi, Bert Brookes and Hilda Hamer. The three Italians, from No. 2 P.O.W. Hostel on the Leominster road, came daily to work on the farm.

'Booking was a pleasant job, particularly in good weather', writes Edith Silcock who worked as a booker in Bishops Frome. 'In wet weather it was not so easy, slipping about in deep mud with rainwater dripping off the bines and trying to hold up an umbrella to keep the rain off the book and cards. After the last bushelling of the day those who had run out of funds would come along for a "sub" and draw a pound or two to keep them going, this too being entered on their card and in the book.

The evening after the yards had been cleared and picking finished was hectic for the booker. The number of bushels entered in the book had to be totalled up for each picker and the amount due calculated. This was far from simple as the price for picking at the start usually changed over the weeks so that one would have to calculate say 157 bushels at seven to the shilling, 97 at six to the shilling and 137 at six and a half to the shilling. After working out a hundred or so similar problems one's head became a little muzzy. And all this before the days of pocket calculators! The only help to hand was a well thumbed ready reckoner. Then the subs had to be totalled and subtracted and in some cases this total was almost as much as the amount earned and there was little to take home.

The following morning the money for paying the pickers had to be fetched from the bank in Worcester. Permission was obtained from the police to park outside the bank and a constable would be on hand while the money was loaded into the car. It amounted to several thousands of pounds, quite a lot of it in silver or copper, so was quite heavy to handle.

Bushelling at Little Froome. Flo Preece booking, Adam Jones bushelling and Leonard Lock holding the sack already half full. Ada Powell at the far end of the crib.

Booking in the rain at Ullingswick.

Then there was the paying out. A table was set up and the farmer and booker presided at this while each card holder came up in turn, produced their card, the amount due to them was looked up in the book and the farmer counted out their money. When all had been paid they loaded themselves and their belongings into the buses sent for them and set off back to their homes in South Wales. Everyone relaxed, breathed a sigh of relief and another hop picking was over!'

On some farms strikes for more money seemed to occur every year, but never lasted long. At Little Froome, Thursdays were particularly prone to strikes, as Bromyard Market was close at hand and there were bargains to be had. While at Instone Court there used to be a ritual confrontation with Sidney Parker which would start noisily but usually end with jokes and laughing and a visit to 'The Tiddly', the Holly Bush: drinks all round on the 'Gaffer' and, weather permitting, the pickers would be back at work the next day. Sometimes the strike went on for another twenty-four hours but this was rare. Very often a rise in the picking rate was obtained—but not always. During the war Mildred Shepherd picked approximately two bushels for a shilling and 'any farmer who gave less was liable to have a strike on his hands.'

Gypsies helped with the hops at Garford, Yarkhill, in the early '50s recalls Margaret Dallow, 'There were thirty-five acres of hops (that is hop acres—1000 stocks to a hop acre). There would be thirty-six caravans and about forty horses, however after a bit of horse trading and when the lights of the farmhouse had gone out, twenty or thirty more horses might appear. In the morning they would hotly deny there were any extra! One day Granny Smith arrived, two thin plaits looped about her ears and her skirt to the ground, and asked if she could bring her family to work in the hopyards. She had four sons with names like Geldin and Jobie and three daughters. The young women, all with good figures, often had a baby on one arm enveloped in a blanket, leaving the other free to work. They would work very hard at the hop tying, etc, the whole family taking part and doing two fields to the one of the Welsh, but when the time came for them to go to Evesham they would leave. In the middle of August they would return to help finish the harvest and make ready for hop picking. In September their numbers would be swollen with pickers from the Welsh valleys, 200 adults and nearly 100 children, and on a Sunday evening the singing from the covered cowshed was beautiful. The gypsies held the ''Master'', as they called my father, in great respect and if he went out the gypsy women would patrol the farmhouse to see that my mother and sister and I were all right.'

As a lively conclusion to the old days, Ethel Paske recalls an incident when, owing to the decrease in the local labour force, more gypsies were also being employed at Little Froome: 'On one occasion someone from Highwell House (which overlooks the farm) rang the police to say that murder was being committed at Little Froome. Because my husband was ill I met the police when they arrived and went with them to the gypsies' caravans. The police put the troublemakers into their caravans and I stood watching, couldn't do anything else, for as fast as they were put in at the front they got out at the back!'

Change was taking place by the 1950s, however, and the number of pickers began to dwindle. The war had brought about an increase in regular employment for women, and the local education authorities in the Black Country and Herefordshire, once so co-operative, ruled that their school terms and holidays should be the same as the rest of the country. When picking by hand finally came to an end in the district, about 1970 at Avenbury Court, there were many, nevertheless, who sorely missed the opportunity of working in the hopyards.

Hop Pole Creosote Tank
at Huntlands Farm, Whitbourne

CHAPTER 3

They was Lovely Days

'In the week all Bromyard went down to Little Froome and Avenbury Court at six or seven o'clock in the morning out across the fields.'

Layton Edwards, 1985.

As the year begins to turn into Autumn and there is a certain misty freshness in the morning air with the promise of warmth later on, local people still say, "It's a real hop-picking morning". They seem to sniff the air and nod in agreement that whatever they are about to do they would much rather be setting off to the hopyard for a day's hop picking, as they would have done thirty or forty years ago.

The majority of the pickers were women and children, in most cases setting out to earn a much welcomed supplement to the family income; a winter coat, a shedful of coal, new furniture or the school uniform for a scholarship child. How the mothers enjoyed this money, particularly because it was theirs to spend as they wished on their own special security or luxury. For three or four weeks all household chores laid aside, they set out with their macs and stools, sandwich boxes and old kitchen knives to take up residence in the hopyard houses, in a different community bound by strict rules enforced by the polepullers and a timetable dictated by the busheller and the drying kilns.

Hop picking meant getting up early in the morning to go and meet the lorry at the end of the road or to take the long walk to Paskes at Little Froome. Everyone wore old clothes with long sleeves and trousers or thick stockings to prevent the bines from scratching and scarring bare arms and legs. These clothes held the scent of the hops until the season came round again. An old pram or pushchair was essential equipment for the little ones and the day's supplies. Also needed were extra coats in case of rain and an umbrella, the tin biscuit box with scones or cake for 'bait time' and sandwiches for dinner (not forgetting a damp cloth to clean the worst of the stains from your hands before eating), and tea, sugar and lemonade crystals for the children. Milk and drinking water could be fetched from the farm but the Thermos was filled for the first warm drink of the day before any fires were lit to boil the big black kettles. In case of cuts and scratches there would be some Elastoplast or a bandage with lint, and the washing blue bag in a damp piece of muslin to ease the pain of wasp stings.

Good hop-picking stools were made locally, some by Ernie (Jim) Dallow at Sirrells the blacksmiths. They were all tall enough to enable the picker to sit well up to the crib and had a ledge on which to rest the feet and help to stop the legs of the stool sinking into the soil. A short-bladed kitchen knife was stuck in the end post of the crib for slicing the bines before pulling them from the overhead wire and cutting them into manageable pieces in the crib.

Miss Walton and May with a half-end folding crib.

Arthur Berry, a baker at Weale and Bateman, taking his holiday to pick hops with Elsie and the family.

Mary Pearson booking, Adam Jones bushelling and David Paske holding a greensack at Little Froome.

Older, retired men or those able to take their holidays helped to make up the numbers. A family would have one or two cribs, but a woman on her own would share a half-end with a friend or neighbour. It was important to pick fast enough to keep up with everyone else when the cribs were moved up the yard as each house was cleared.

On the first day, with crib allocated and set out in the dense greenery of the fresh hopyard, voices were muffled and you could not see who was around you, but as the bines were pulled your neighbours came gradually into view to be hailed and greeted as if encountered in a foreign land. The firm hops gradually covered the hessian of the crib and grew into a bright mound until the warning, "Clear 'em up", came from the busheller and heralded his approach. No leaves, dirt or pieces of bine must remain in the crib when the busheller, bin men and the booker arrived. Measured into the sacks, bushelled 'light' or 'heavy' the hops were cleared to a last half measure, your bin card with your number on the front and the rules on the back recorded the morning's picking and it was bait time .... but not for long ... the hungry kilns were awaiting your labours, cut, pull, spray and pick again.

NOTICE.

Pickers are responsible for the loss of this Book and all money due thereon will be paid to bearer only.

1. Any person accepting this book and proceeding to pick shall be deemed to have agreed to and be bound by the undermentioned rules.

2. The hops must be picked clean and free from bine and leaves, and unless so picked they will be removed from the cribs without being measured, and the pickers will not be entitled to be paid for picking them.

3. The employer shall (in addition to all other rights) have the right of discharging any picker or pickers for bad picking or refusing to clean up the cribs for measuring, or to pick up loose hops when required, or who are guilty of any misconduct or interference with other pickers, or who are found smoking in Rickyard or Farm buildings.

4. Pickers dismissed for misconduct, or refusing to remain throughout the whole of the picking, to be paid at reduced rate and to forfeit any allowances.

5. The employer to have full power to engage any fresh pickers he may require during the progress of the picking.

☞ Take notice that all persons guilty of taking away poles, fruit, or of any illegal act, will be prosecuted.

16

TILLEY'S

Hop-Picker's Account Book.

No. of Crib *16*

Name of Picker _____

_____

No. at Crib *2*

MANUFACTURED BY

L. TILLEY & SON, Ltd.,

Printers & Stationers,

LEDBURY.

Reg, Freda and Bryon Eversham, and Elaine Cross. Bryon and Elaine are picking into an umbrella, while in the background the polepuller is tidying a fallen bine.

As the house was picked you emerged into the open world where voices were clearer and the cart with the sacks could be seen. Also visible were the polepullers crossing the mounds with their long handled tools, taking down the flags—those few sprays left waving on the wire—and turning over the piles of picked bines in case hops were dropped or wasted. Mothers in old raincoats and felt hats or wrap-around aprons called to collect up their brood and encourage or bribe them to pick another few boxes or umbrellas full before the busheller came round again. When every bine was cleared it was time to plunge once again into the dense green of a new house, the polepullers carrying the crib and all of us trailing behind with our paraphernalia.

After dinner some children would play or go to fetch dry sticks to replenish the fire. Blackberries, and nuts ripening in the hedgerows, mushrooms and windfall apples or pears were all fair game if no damage was done to the trees. It was considered lucky if you found a 'silver grub', the chrysalis of a moth or butterfly hidden on the underside of a leaf, to be taken home in a jam jar and kept in the hope that it might hatch.

The farmyard and buildings were forbidden territory and certain quiet areas behind hedges were designated to provide for ''nature's needs'' where a plentiful supply of dock leaves was considered a necessity.

Loading greensacks.

L. to r. Gladys Bedford, ?, Joyce Blything, Mrs Blything, Maud Evans, Bill Evans, Michael Passey, Danny Hill, Emmy Wall (sitting), Iris Wall, Dolly Corbett, and Anita and Elaine Wall.

After the last of the day's bushellings the trek home began and many a local father had cooked the tea for the pickers' return. The corner shops were busy and stayed open especially late with supplies of sausages, bacon, cheese and corned beef ready for the next day's bait.

It is hard to describe the special atmosphere or camaraderie of the individual hopyards—a sense of belonging to a group with certain customs of their own. The polepullers had a certain status, at once authoritarian yet familiar, and as the last bines were pulled a particular custom called cribbing was observed. This was when the unmarried girls were ceremoniously 'dumped' into the crib. Who was chosen, or how, one never knew but sounds of a scuffle and cries of protest would be heard as the unsuspecting girl would be approached from each side, usually by the polepullers or binmen, lifted into the air and dropped into the few hops left in the crib. Her shrieks and cries would be accompanied by cheers and laughter as the ancient rite was fulfilled. Sometimes the girls got together and up-ended the binman in a crib. Another custom was to cure a few whole bines in the kiln to be used at harvest festival and also to decorate the bar at the local pub.

Hop pillows were a favourite remedy for insomnia as the heady scent of the dried hops was claimed to be sleep-inducing.

Cribbing the unmarried girls! (Lena Partridge, Adam Jones and Kate Partridge - later Mrs Sam Jones).

Above right Rose James, Callis James, Lil Page Jones, Elsie Armstrong, Jessie Taylor, Emily Young. *Front* Marianne Paske and Adam Jones.

Below right Revenge - cribbing a young man at Newton Farm in the 1940s.

Sunday was a different day in the hopyard—a late start and always lots of visitors. This was the day many of our photographs were taken which explains why some of the subjects are very nicely dressed, and in the earlier pictures even appear to be wearing their best hats. It was 'not done' to visit and not pick a few sprays. With the extra family members adding to the hands around the crib, by three or four o'clock the polepullers would call loudly, 'No more bines, no more bines', and woe betide anyone who pulled down some more as this was the signal that the kilns were full and there were more than enough hops to be dried during the night. Sunday was a short and festive day and many people's most vivid memories are of those visits to the hopyard.

The Red Cross or Meals on Wheels benefited from the voluntary pickers who often spent days in the hopyard working at the charity crib, and it was customary for the regulars to pick a bushel or two, now and again, as their contribution.

A good picker could pick about 20-25 bushels a day when the hops were firm and the weather fine, but a good picker would also pick through bad weather and even help to clear hops when the wirework had come down and the farmer had a difficult harvest.

Molly Littlehales, Arthur Barlow, Gladys Smith and Susan Hill at the Meals on Wheels charity crib.

Daphne Davies's vivid childhood memories are followed by more from another local picker who remembers: 'Hop picking in the 1920s when I was a child. It was a lovely holiday as we had six weeks holiday from school in September to go hop picking. We had to be up early mornings and it was cold to go out; we had to wear warm coats as we had more than a mile to walk to Mr Adams, Avenbury Court. We always went there, there were other hopyards, Mr Price, Little Froome, Cooks the Brook House, Buckles the Hyde. The mothers took a basket with a loaf of bread, lump of butter, cheese, and perhaps a cake.....

It soon came lunchtime; some people used to light a nice fire and boil their kettle for a cup of tea, do some toast, perhaps hold a slice of bacon on a stick over the fire, sometimes a kipper. It used to get a bit black but they still ate it as it smelled so nice. The children loved having a fire to have a warm by.

Sometimes you sat on some wires and picked the hops in a box or an umbrella, it gave you a rest as if you kept picking in the crib and looked about your mothers used to give you a nip across your hand and tell you to get on with picking, as when you had done one house you moved to a new one to start again.

Two or three men came a few times round the crib giving out booklets on God and preached to you, if you took no notice of them they would call you a sinner, they expected you to stand and listen to them. There was a vicarage at the top of the hopyard and the parson used to come with a basket of apples or plums and give you a few; they did not taste very nice as your hands were black and tasted of hops.

As years went by the hops went up in price to 3/- a bushel and the farmer would pay for two buses to take you into the hopyard and back about 5 o'clock at night.

When all the hopyards were picked you went to the farm to be paid and have a lump of fruit cake and a drink, they was lovely days.'

This happy group, including Rose Hicks and Eva Walwyn, en-joying a cup of tea on paying-out day.

As a schoolgirl in the '30s Edith Silcock picked in the Teme Valley where: 'The pickers came from the Black Country, mostly from the Lye and Dudley areas. They lived in the "barracks" and were a rough, tough crowd. Their language was colourful, to say the least. the favourite word being bloody but one rarely heard any "four-letter" words. Several members of the Salvation Army lived with them in the barracks looking after their social welfare and carrying out any necessary first aid. At the weekends buses arrived laden with their friends and relations from the Black Country and at this time things were liable to disappear—fruit from the trees, chickens from their runs and even washing from the line! They always brought their dogs with them, usually lurchers, and had a great time poaching rabbits.

The local (home) pickers were collected by bus from various pick-up points and taken to the hopyard. One of the first things to do on arriving at the crib was to make a fire with any available bits of wood, particularly on cold mornings when there was sometimes ice on the hops. After picking for an hour or so it was time for breakfast....

The bushellers usually came round three times a day. We had two in our yard, Mr D. and Mr. J. Mr D was the local publican. He was large and jolly, and wore an old khaki shirt, baggy tweed trousers held up by large braces and nearly splitting apart over his ample middle, and an old battered trilby hat. He only laughed

Charlie Hodges bushelling at Mintridge in the 1920s.

Mintridge, Stoke Lacy, with the hop kiln next to the house.

when the women complained that he bushelled too heavily and he could hold his own when it came to bawdy comments or blue stories. Mr J. was quite the opposite being thin and wiry. He wore a cap which he turned back to front so that the peak did not get in the way as he lifted the bushel full of hops to tip into the sack the men were holding ready to receive them. He rarely smiled and did not indulge in any back-chat with the pickers. If they got too cheeky he would, accidentally of course, catch them on the head with the bushel as he bent over to take the hops out of the crib. This would lead to a stream of bad language and unfavourable comments on his parentage but he took no notice and just continued on his way.

During the afternoon various vans would visit the hopyard looking for customers, the butcher, the baker, ice cream van, etc, and the Salvation Army lassies brought along a large urn of tea on a barrow. This had a distinctive taste to it and the general opinion was that it tasted of iodine, this being due, it was said, to the urn being used to boil up the bandages used in the first aid activities. However, there were always plenty of customers when the cry of "tea-oh" was heard along the headland.

After the late afternoon bushelling everyone went home to clean up and get a cooked meal. Cleaning one's hands, which were coated with a thick film of pollen from the hops, was a problem and everyone had their favourite solution varying from washing them in paraffin to smearing them liberally with butter.'

Mollie Walwyn's first memories of hop picking were: 'Watching the Black Country pickers arriving at Bromyard Station by special train and of the farm drays awaiting them. Their tin trunks were loaded with them and taken to several farms for about three weeks picking.

When I was a little older my family went "hopping" to the Brook House, Avenbury, owned by Alfred and John Cook. We had to walk there and back and usually started out in the dark about 6 a.m. My sister, much younger than I, had a wooden truck made from an old pram to ride in.

My father who was a postman saved his holidays to come with us. The money earned usually bought us new shoes etc for the winter. Old clothes were kept during the year to wear in the fields and we waited for the "umbrella man" to come to Bromyard some weeks previously. He would exchange broken "brollies" for mended ones and the large man's umbrella was so useful in helping to keep us dry when it rained.

Some pickers took a short cut over the fields by the "Haunted Church" but it was too creepy early in the morning so round the road we went. "Strangers", as we called them lived in the buildings. One I remember very well. He was called

Mollie Walwyn picking at Little Froome in the 1950s. Bill Evans, Mollie, Eva Walwyn behind Maud Evans, and Violet Lock.

In 1940 Ethel Waldron of Burley Gate Post Office drove a van shop, a converted ambulance, for the hop pickers. She used to call at Hillhampton at dinner time, and farms in Much Cowarne and Moreton Jeffries in the evenings, returning to the shop about 10.30 p.m. Here she is at Leighton Court, Much Cowarne.

"Darkie" and came every year with his wife to the Brook House. He would help us get a dry faggot of wood to light our fire. We boiled our kettle on an iron rack over the fire and toasted bread and rashers of bacon on a stick, catching the fat on the bread. It tasted grand. Milk could be had from the farm. Mr Alf Cook did the measuring by bushel basket himself.

Years later I used to go with a mobile shop from Burtons Stores to Instone Court to supply the pickers who lived in the farm buildings during the picking. Tom Corbett drove the van and we went there three days a week. Later still I went hopping again with my baby son. It was wartime and the Battle of Britain was raging. Every time we heard a plane we mothers grabbed the babies and tried to hide under the hop bines. Mr Robinson, a schoolmaster, used to give us each day the number of enemy planes that had been brought down during the previous day to cheers from all of us. We sometimes went to other farms to help out if we finished ours first.

Hopping to us was a real holiday, especially if the weather was good, but rain or shine we all looked forward to it.'

Following Mollie Walwyn's memories of travelling with the mobile shop, Layton Edwards recalls how Glen Warburton and he used to take a 30 cwt van to stock up the local shops such as the Major's Arms on Fromes Hill, the Fir Tree, the Five Bridges, Hope's Rough by Bromtrees Hall and the Post Offices at Bishops Frome and Burley Gate.

'The local traders also took vans out to the hopyards and especially to supply the farm "shops" such as those at Nevilles the Dovehills and Yates the Venn. The orders were much sought after, but most farmers went to their regular grocers. The vans took bulk orders, say ½ cwt of sugar in ½ lb and 1 lb packets. Tea at 5d a quarter, a whole cheese to be cut up with knives or the shopkeeper loaned them a cheesewire. Sliced bacon was in 5 lb packs to be sold to the pickers by the slice. Woodbines were 250 for 7/- when 5 in a packet, 200 for 5/- when 10 in a packet. Twist was 8d an ounce and Best Shag 8½d an ounce.

Saturday afternoon was time off in the hopyards. Many families stayed on the farms to do their washing, cook a special meal and rest, or they could attend the mission meetings, often organised by the Salvation Army. Others collected their "subs" and went to town. Bromyard was like a beehive, you couldn't move for people in the streets and all the pub yards were full of carts and drays. The women shopped and the men went on the scrumpy. Only the local people were allowed in the bars, so the pickers bought their drinks at the jug and bottle and drank in the pub yards.

The local policemen supplemented by the specials were constantly on patrol. Rumours of fights and knifings abounded and even the women would fight with much swearing and hair pulling, often "egged on" by their menfolk. Too much rough cider was blamed for such behaviour.'

HOP PICKERS' BARRACKS. (OLD)
Much Cowarne. Herefs.

CHAPTER 4

Clear 'Em Up!

In the researches for this book, letters were written to some of the Birmingham and Black County newspapers asking people to write their memories of hop picking before the days of the machine. We were surprised to get such a large response to our enquiries and find what happy memories the old hop-picking days evoked. Of course, these letters are from older people who came hop picking as children and perhaps remember the old days with childhood affection; to their mothers hops meant hard work in good weather and bad, and a few shillings towards the family needs.

We have had to pick extracts from these letters but have tried to keep their flavour, so evocative of a past era. The editor of *The Birmingham Post & Mail*, Keith Whetstone, was the first to reply with his experiences at Nashend Farm during the Second World War.

'Although I have no experience of Bromyard, I do have lasting memories of two summers spent on a farm at Bosbury between Ledbury and Hereford, when I was 10 and 11 .... Apart from us kids and a few family friends, the hop pickers were Land Army girls, brought in to replace the gypsies who had traditionally provided the labour before the war. I remember Farmer Davies moaning that he never had to make any provision for the gypsies, but he had been forced to provide a proper hut and other facilities as living quarters for the girls.

Keith Whetstone and his brother with the Women's Land Army girls at Nashend Farm, Bosbury, about 1941. It is unusual to see W.L.A. girls wearing their hats, and one suspects that the photograph was taken on a special occasion.

I have other memories of those days—the desperate scrounging of fuel to keep the donkey engine going in the oast house; visits from my parents and friends at week-ends when we all tested our gas masks in the sulphur-laden fumes of the drying furnace room....

My, you have brought back memories. I've just recalled how we used to dig our arms into the crib and raise the hops in an attempt to lighten them just before the measuring bushel came round in the hope that they'd go further. I think we were paid 4d a bushel, but memory may have misled me.'

Once the Society's letter appeared in the press, replies came in thick and fast. The next one takes us back to the 1920s.

'I do have a few memories of the hop picking days. Sorry I have no printed facts nor photographs of those days, just memories which may help you to pursue the history and character of the farms.

As most hop pickers came from the Black Country it meant each farmer had an agent who recruited labour, namely pickers and men to cut the wires (bines) and work in the kilns.

These agents were women, who were also pickers, they organised the whole picking season from beginning to end, no mean thing you will see.

Hop pickers in the 1920s.

Having recruited the required number of *good* pickers, she had to see that all boxes and pickers were at the railway station waiting for the train, she would see all the belongings were loaded on the train. The excitement and noise were always almost indescribable. Many of those women and children had hardly moved out of their Road or Street since the last hop picking season—it was indeed a working holiday. The road leading to the railway station would be a sight worth seeing, almost every contraption on wheels was used to convey the boxes to the station, such as wheelbarrows, tramways, dobbins, high prams, horse and gigs, horse and traps.

The clatter of hob nailed or iron tipped shoes added to the noise. Many a man had a day off from work to see their wives and children on their way.

In those days the journey to Hereford was a long one, so we were very happy to arrive: Captain Edwards (who farmed at Lower Town, Preston Wynne) would have two or three hay carts waiting at the station to take us to the farm; first the boxes would be placed in the carts, then we would sit on them to enjoy another slow ride along narrow lanes, offtime we would have to duck under the overhanging trees, mostly fruit trees, the high hedgerows were covered with blackberries and hazel nuts.

The last lap of the journey - leaving Stoke Edith Station for the farm around 1908.

Mr Jim Soley and Mr Powell bushelling hops at Poplands about 1950. The strings were for tying the greensacks.

On arrival at the farm boxes would be taken into the barn, most women were very strong. Clean straw would be placed on the floor, a sheet or blanket was placed over the straw, pillows placed in position and then other clothes. Next item was to meet the Captain to discuss how many bushels to the shilling. Some women inspected the hops then decided whether to accept the offer or not, the Captain gave a speech of welcome, asked us not to take apples from the trees on account of damage to the tree. He gave us the promise he would sell at the end of the picking season as many apples as we wanted, at a very cheap price; he was always true to his word. He also said if we boys helped to pick up potatoes on a Saturday afternoon every person would have a Saturday dinner.

We boys and girls went to a little church there never seemed a welcome or any encouragement. The Salvation Army came every week and gave everyone a real happy hour, the singing and preaching in the farmyard broke the silence of the countryside. The first week or so many pickers could not sleep, the silence was too much.

Now for the cribs, there were three kinds, the small, the large with a partition and the large without the partition.

Sometimes Captain Edwards busheled the hops, he was a very light busheler. His son a very heavy one and suffered the curses of the women, and they could swear.

Neither father or son would bushel dirty hops—that is a crib of hops containing leaves.

Pickers' hands would become yellow with stain, food touched by those hands would be bitter. Mornings would be very cold, afternoons very hot.'

Another letter from Birmingham.

'My parents took me hop picking before I was old enough for school. My family, relations, friends, neighbours. We went from Snow Hill Station Birmingham from the first week in September, Sunday or Monday morning about eight o'clock. I was only a small child but people waiting on the platform or getting off the trains would look at us as tho' we had come from out of space. It used to have Hop Pickers Only on the train windows and we would be shunted off and left for some time while the other trains went through. We used to go for two or

Wagonloads of hop pickers leaving Bromyard Station for the hop farms.

Pickers from Birmingham in the hopyards at Whitbourne in the 1920s.

three or more weeks till the hop picking was finished. To Mr Twinberrow's, White House Farm, Suckley near Worcester and Bromyard till the time I got married, nothing could keep us away. It was our working holiday. We looked forward to it from the time we came home we were waiting to get back next year. We had lots of friends, who ever got there first would have the fires lit outside our barns which we lived in…. Twinberrow had two sons, Kim and Jack. They done the busheling about three times a day. Then every other night when it was time to knock off one of them would come round to our cribs to give us a sub. We would go to the shops, my mum would cook us a dinner on the fire outside our barn. My dad and his mates would go to have a drink at the pub, The Crosskeys, just past our shop on the hill, if you walked straight on you would come to Bromyard. We used to go there to the shops of a Saturday afternoon. People came from other parts of Birmingham and from the Black Country, West Bromwich, Cradley Heath, Dudley, Walsall. Some people came every year.

Men came down the field selling hot doughnuts, lardy cakes, ice cream, sweets and shout ''Cry Baby. Cry, if your mother won't buy you some sweets. Hot faggots and peas.'' My mum used to take the basins and spoons down the field and bread. We all worked hard so we had good food and enjoyed it singing while we picked the hops, ''Here comes the busheler to bushel up your hops'' and ''We are the New York dandies.'' Everyone joined in, never a dull moment. We used to have a barn dance up at the Crosskeys Pub Saturday night….'

A letter from Dudley emphasises the need to earn money in the hard times before the War.

'The first time I ever went hop picking I was ten years old. 1939 War was just breaking out, but that didn't really bother me, I didn't realise how awful the War would be, I was so excited to be going hopping as my mother called it. She was a widow with a family to bring up and was desperately hard up so our next door neighbour suggested hop picking. Mother was rather reluctant, she thought only common people went, but anyway poverty won and we were on our way in an old bone shaker of a coach, but us kids thought it was great, we had never been on holiday in our lives and to us we were having a month's holiday. It seemed to take hours to get to the farm (The Farm, Moreton Jeffries), it was owned by Mr Harry and Jack Baskerville not far from Bromyard, a place called Stoke Lacy. I was rather surprised to see we were to be living in a barn and sleeping on a straw bed, but it was only the thought of earwigs that bothered me. We settled down very well, there were big iron grates and we had the most beautiful coke fires, we could use as much coke as we liked. We didn't much care for getting up at the crack of dawn, but the smell of bacon and eggs cooking gave us a healthy appetite. After breakfast we would wash up and mother would cut a pile of sandwiches to take to the hopfields complete with kettle of water, tea, sugar and milk. By the time I had carried the kettle of water and picked a few apples there was usually only half a kettle of water left.

Although we were only children we were expected to work all day long, except for dinner hour—ours was usually two hours because my brother and I used to have to fetch firewood to light the fire in the hopyard on which to boil the kettle, but once we could get away from work we used to go into the orchard for apples—I remember eating 10 apples one day with no affect on my stomach.

Mr Baskerville, both Harry and Jack, were very nice, they didn't mind anyone having the apples so long as the trees were not damaged. On Sunday mornings Harry would let everyone have as many potatoes they needed and didn't charge anything for them. Also, every Sunday he would sell rabbits for about 6d and 9d each, and carrots and onions. We used to have rabbit stew, my mother was a smashing cook, they tasted really good and we would follow on with lovely apple dumpling. We were extremely healthy kids, and we were always kept very clean and tidy.

We used to wait for the ice cream van to come to the hopfields so that we could have a 1d wafer, and about two fields away there was a little pub called the Three Crowns. We used to fetch fresh crusty bread from there, also Smith's crisps at 1d per packet. Some of the neighbours used to come into the fields to pick hops. One dear old lady used to bring tomatoes from her greenhouse to sell 4d per pound. The Septembers then were beautiful, it hardly ever rained, we used to be as brown as berries. We even used to pray for rain so that we could play instead of picking hops, although most of the time we really worked hard for our mother because we knew the money would be for our new winter clothes for school.

About three nights each week it would be Sub Night, that meant you could sub some of the money you had earned to keep yourselves. Every Sub Night I would

Mrs Morgan frying on a brazier or 'devil' - under cover but not in the barn for fear of fire in the buildings.

A hop picker cooking for her family at Stanford Court.

go and hide because I didn't want to be seen fetching money. I used to think it was very degrading but my mother only used to have 10/- widow's pension plus 5/- for my brother and 3/- each for my sister and myself, and used to have to pay 11/3 rent out of that, no wonder she used to have to take washing and sewing in to make ends meet. No rent rebate or family allowance in those days.

After that first year my mother went every year. I used to pack my job up to go till I was 18 years old. I'd soon get another job within a few days of getting home.

It used to be lovely at night, we would sit around the fires singing all the old songs and about 9.30 p.m. Harry would come and pour water on all the fires because of air raids, and we used to go to bed.

It was amazing really, so many people living rough and yet everyone got on so well, never any rows or trouble, and the men had their own sleeping quarters. Not even married couples could sleep together. The women's room was quite a distance from the men's. When we were coming home the farmer would sell best apples very cheap, also Victoria plums 1d per pound. I had to fetch 24 lbs once for making jam at the grand total of 2/-. Although I have enough money now to go on holiday anywhere in the world, I could never ever be so happy as I was down on Baskerville's farm.'

In similar vein and expressing very vividly the urgent excitement of childhood comes this letter from Tipton.

'.... My mother, brother, grandma and I went hop picking every year for over 25 years and to the same farm. It was just outside the Bromyard area (Hill Farm, Stanley Hill, Bosbury). Miss Cotton and her niece, Nan Clews, ran the farm. Two wonderful and kindly ladies. I remember Miss Cotton as a very old lady who wore a long black dress with a white apron over it. In her pocket she always carried mints and used to give us poor kids a few nearly every day. Miss Nan (as we called her) was such a kindly person also. She always had a smile and a kind word for us. She inherited the farm when Miss Mary Ann Cotton passed away. The farm was rather small with just two hopyards. Therefore about 25 people used to go for the hop picking. The same families turned up every year. In fact, it was like meeting one's own family once a year. There was also Mr and Mrs Dixon, they were gypsies, they also came every year with their family and parked their caravan in a field behind the kilns.

From June the only thing in our minds was how long before we were to go on our annual holiday to the hopyards. We counted the days, getting prepared a few days before the final day arrived was so exciting. Mother would check the old tin hop picking box to see what bit of tin food she had collected to take with us. There never was a great deal as my dad was on the means test and the money we had to live on wasn't much. We relied on neighbours and relatives to give us a bit of sugar or a quarter of tea and such like to take with us. At last the great day arrived, the night before we would have had a bath in the old tin tub before the fire, mother would take a last look in our hair to see that we had no nits and so to bed, not to sleep, we were much too excited to sleep, thinking of the great day ahead. Up at six (the train was about 10 a.m. we didn't want to be late). Dad would borrow the neighbour's trolley to take the hop picking box to the station. At last there we were on the platform waiting with all our friends from last year for the train. Here it comes. Oh the excitement, mother makes sure the box is put in a safe place in the guard's van. Into the carriage we all get and off we go. On the journey we kids would be planning what we were going to do when we got to paradise (that was what the dear old farm was to us).

When we were well on our way, out of her basket mother would get the loaf and a jam jar, the jar was filled with margarine, she would then proceed to cut two hunks of bread and marge. We would relish it. She would say, ''That will last you until we get there.''

Then arriving at Ledbury station out of the station we kids would rush to see if the farmhands, Mike Palmer and Mr Jenkins was there with the two great shire horses and farm cart. Sure enough, there they would be on the forecourt. Back to the station we would run to help to carry the boxes for them to be loaded onto the cart. Sitting on the boxes and away we would go to travel five miles this way .....'

Here is a memory from a man living in Rowley Regis who went hop picking before the First World War.

'Hop picking was a delight to us children, we looked forward to it more than Xmas. Oddly enough my first hop picking trip is my best remembered. It was before the First World War. I think 1912 .... I think why I remember so long ago is because an incident happened one day. My mother had got my youngest brother to sleep and lay him in the hop vines, out of the sun. Presently the big cart horse that collected the bags of hops stopped dead and would not move, everybody was saying what's wrong with the horse he's never been like that before, then my mother shouted with horror, ''My child is nearly under the cart wheel.'' The horse knew that and was fed with apples for days after.

About ½ mile up the road was a little shop and a kindly woman served me with some things. After that she took my dry bread sandwich off me and put a slice of meat in between, and several times after. People were very good then. Every evening after work, the master would dish out jugs of cider and firewood for our fires at night. Any eggs the fowls had laid away under the hedgerows we could keep. That and collecting apples to take back home was my job. .... I remember the big walnut tree at the bottom of the drive. We used to throw up at them to knock them off for Xmas and get our hands covered in walnut stains. Then the master would say, ''See you have been at my nuts again.'' He had a lot of guinea fowl, they would fly on to the barns and make a cry like, ''Come back! Come back!'' People would shout, ''We will! We will!''

Collecting greensacks at Merryfield, Stoke Lacy. Esne Jones at the horse's head.

Another nonagenarian looks back.

'As I shall be 90 years of age this November 18th (1984) your letter to the Birmingham Post Tuesday November 13th (1984) brought back to me vivid memories of living in Bromyard as a young child. I think I was only 7 or 8 when we left Bromyard for Birmingham. As a child I suffered from anaemia badly and my mother was told that I should be taken to the hopfields from sunrise to sunset for the good of my health, and when the school holidays started off we went, Mother, a brother two years older and another brother 2½ years younger. If the hop picking season was not finished when the school holiday was over that school holiday was extended much to our delight. Given fine weather it was a delightful time for all of us...

We children took old umbrellas which were opened and the ends stuck into the ground, and we picked into those earning a few coppers occasionally when we were not foraging around the fields for apples.

I think my memory is right in saying that the price then for picking was 8 pennies a bushel, a straight up wicket basket—it did take a long time to pick a bushel.

The women pickers chatted and seemed a happy crowd. The farmer brought round churns of hot milk about mid morning and when we had a break to eat I can remember the joy of eating herrings and bloaters toasted over a sort of camp fire.

At sunset we packed up and walked home quite a long way, very grubby and very tired.

When all the hop picking was over an old custom took place. All the farm men who had cut down the bines, measured the bushels or picked hops and carted them away, had their fun. They cribbed all the old ladies, which meant they up-ended them into the cribs—a sight not to be forgotten.

A very dim memory, I can remember standing in the Square end of the main street for celebrating the Relief of Mafeking.

Also my two brothers and myself had Scarlet Fever and we were taken to the fever hospital at the foot of the Downs where we were fed on milk puddings for weeks and weeks and chickens wandered in and out of the ward, all still a vivid memory.'

A letter full of incident and wealth of detail came from West Bromwich.

'I was interested in your letter in the Express and Star and I hope this may be of some help to your worthy effort to portray the life in the hopfields around Bromyard. I am 58 years old and went hop picking when I was born and many times from then on. I was left in my pushchair in the middle of a field at Tenbury when my mother was chased by a very angry bull. I was then 18 months old and needless to say, I survived that not very nice ordeal. At that time parties of pickers went from all over the Black Country, about 40 strong. They were organized by a leader who had been appointed by the hop grower, usually someone who had gone for donkeys' years as they used to say .... Some travelled by train to Stour-bridge junction and on to Stourport. There they were met by farm carts and taken to their farms. People from different areas went to their particular farms and were known as the Tipton lot, Cradley and Old Hill lot, Smethwick lot, Bromsgrove lot and so on. They mostly consisted of women and older men. Only a few younger men went and a good few of these were men who strangely enough would not work at home although there were jobs. They were called Rodneys in the Black Country slang. That is not to say they were all idlers as there were no easy jobs in the hopyards.... Children, as in my case, were not allowed to leave until they had picked a quota set by their mothers. The best part of the day was when tea was brewed and sandwiches handed out; bread and jam was the normal thing and wasps created a nuisance—I've had many a painful sting. The stains on the fingers tasted very bitter from the hops but it was not often we could wash our hands, nevertheless we enjoyed our food. One of the worst aspects of the picking was rainy weather but it was no excuse to stop work unless of course it was too extreme. The red sticky mud was awful sometimes inches deep and towards the end of hop picking it was not unknown to find ice on the hops. Usually people

This yard in Acton Beauchamp may have been strung using the Butcher system of wirework invented in Kent in 1875, in which there were three horizontal wires: at ground level, waist high and at the top of the poles. Coir strings for each stock were taken to the middle wire and then sloped to the top wire of the adjacent row. The kettle hangs over the fire ready to replenish the teapot, however Nurse Powell has brought her own thermos.

Hop pickers' quarters at Suckley. This hut was considered a superior type for conscientious pickers only. The kitchen on the left was only partly enclosed. Mr and Mrs Griffiths with their grandchildren, about 1960.

picked five and a half days with the weekend optional; some picked on the weekends and the hops had to stay in the cribs until Monday. Needless to say, some were stolen and put in other cribs by rogues; mostly though so poor, most pickers were honest enough. True there were some riff-raffs who came from all over the country and they gave pickers a bad name. There were some characters and likeable rogues. There were travellers who came year after year and their caravans were so spotless you could eat off the floor. They were not to be confused with tinkers and the like. I made several good lasting friendships with many of the travellers.

Living quarters were rough and sometimes everyone slept in the same barn, divided off by blankets strung over strings. Some were separate stalls with whitewashed walls and clean straw was put on the floors for bedding. The beds were made up in the morning by turning the straw over with a stick. There was not too much privacy in these places and it was embarrassing when the visitors came at weekends, usually the husbands; the sounds of passion were heard very often but in those days the significance escaped me. When we arrived once during the War (1940) the first in got the best places. The farmer who had his place near the Seven Stars and Red Lion at Cradley, handed out a supply of blankets to every one of us. He was classed as a good gaffer. He also gave out a ration of potatoes every day. That year the army were called in to do some picking alongside us which was well appreciated by the teenaged girls (and some cheating women). It was not unusual to see them sneak off among the bushes. The troops had to return to unit every night so they made hay while the sun shone.

There was also a tribe of true Romanies who spoke their own language and had a convoy of horse-drawn caravans—this was a sight to see.

The mornings began when a large fire was made outside the quarters. This was done by a man paid by the pickers themselves; he collected the wood, if it was not supplied by the farmer, chopped it up and put all the smoke-blackened pots, pans and kettles on to boil. This was for washing and making tea. Then there was the delicious smell of bacon cooking to go with the fried eggs; fresh milk was available but I well remember the condensed and evaporated milk. Sandwiches were taken to the hopyards and we had a cooked meal on coming back in the evening, mainly stew made from tinned steak and vegetables bought from the locals very cheaply. The farmer came every night to hand out subs (advances of earnings) to those who wanted money but there was always some to take home at the end of the season.

The Herefordshire House, Stanford Bishop. Mr and Mrs Jones with their daughter Lily.

The pubs in the locality did a roaring trade from the hundreds of pickers. The scrumpy cider was cheap and plentiful and the pubs were lively places to say the least! I have seen many a fight and the main culprits seemed to be the travellers who were banned from some pubs or confined to the bar only. I well remember the Hereford House, the Nelson, Red Lion and Seven Stars all in the Suckley and Cradley areas. My favourite though was Polly Beards' which was a cottage with an off-licence. They sold the brew most of the Black Country people knew. We were served through an open window and drank from bottles we took out of crates; these we washed with water out of a hand pump. We could not drink on the premises so we went through a hole in the hedge to a hopfield twenty yards away. If it was cold (it usually was) the licensee made a huge bonfire and we all sat round and either sang our heads off or listened to the tales told by the travellers. They were varied and always interesting stories of country lore. One man brought a jackdaw with him and he let it fly into the trees until we went home—it talked very well. Old Eva came lunch-time and evening every day to drink her cider. She was a mysterious woman and always sat alone. When she died, the locals collected for her burial.

Polly Beard's Off Licence at Suckley.

A typical group having an evening drink in the hopyard next door to Polly Beard's.

When the hops were finally picked and the day came to go home we said our goodbyes and packed. The trunks were heavy with apples and pears as well as a sprig of hops.

Strangely enough home seemed a luxury what with hot water and baths and home comforts. I still visit there to this day and still see old friends from way back. I also see the ghosts of former characters in my mind's eye....'

It is difficult to follow a letter which brings such a marvellous vibrant picture of hop-picking days but let us look at the other side of the coin and a letter from South Wales presents a much less rosy picture.

'Tredegar in the period 1910 to 1940 sent many families to pick hops. As the season for picking was in September having an extended holiday was looked forward to. Masters and Education Authorities accepted the longer holidays as, sad to say, most of the children hop picking were not very interested in learning. They were conscious of the fact that as children of poor families, work was their future. Grammar school was for those that could afford that kind of life.

The Tredegar areas that provided hop pickers were known as the Back of the Globe, Red Lion Square, Iron Row, Iron Street.

On a Sunday morning in the picking season of 1945 I and some friends travelled to Bromyard to visit the Tredegar people. Quite frankly I was astonished to see the conditions. Stables, cowsheds, barns made up the living quarters. But what jealousy existed as families claimed priority due to the number of years they had worked at this particular farm. There was always an old lady in charge of each family, men stayed at home as they worked in the pits.

Hay and ferns provided the bedding. Sheets, blankets and sacking making a rather uncomfortable bed. It was really great seeing the cooking arrangement. A very large open sided brazier out in the centre of the yard, a roaring log fire and half a dozen frying pans—what a feast, sausage and mash, bacon and boiled spuds and rabbit stew.

Hop Devil.

Toilet facilities were non existent, any bush away from the yard.

On the whole it was looked on first as a holiday in the country, very healthy and a few pounds in the pocket.

At that time gypsies and didicoys were the serious pickers. There was plenty of fights, always during the evenings at the local pubs. Glass smashing became too expensive so landlords introduced a new drinking habit—no pint or half pint glasses, instead a quart jug and half a dozen finger glasses for each table.

There is no doubt this was a working holiday only for the tough, one could not afford to be squeamish or timid. The women folk were able to look after their families and could dish out punishment if needed.

People always criticised the lack of hygiene at the hop fields but the children always looked so healthy on returning home. The sulphur fumes from the kilns being a good cure for many ailments....'

The gang leader who collected people to go hop picking was the very important link between the farmers in the hop picking areas and the hop pickers in the Black Country. Mrs Ann Wright from Dudley was such a gang leader, and her son, Lawson, has provided a good picture.

'She used to pick at Ankerdine Farm, Knightwick before coming to Mr Ted Holloway's farm at The Lower House, Stanford Bishop. Her mother, Mrs Smith, was picking hops in this district as early as 1880-1890. Mrs Smith used to travel from Dudley with a cart drawn by two donkeys. Many hop pickers had their own transport of this sort and their animal stayed with them for the four or five weeks of hop picking.

Many families were self employed and those with horses and carts often dealt in scrap iron, rags, etc. The Guest family had two horses and a covered wagon in which they slept; they were general dealers and regarded as well off. Other families worked in other Black Country trades such as drain making and iron and steel moulding.

During the War Mrs Ann Wright was in war work rope making, but she still brought a gang to Stanford Bishop for their holidays. She used to meet Mr Holloway in the White Horse Inn, Bromyard, in advance and then organised her gang of pickers, probably a dozen or more who were her neighbours or work mates. A gang leader was very particular about the members of the gang as they wanted the work to go well and smoothly. The same people with their families tended to come year after year. Every worker had 12d when they were hired paid by the farmer. When hop picking started the workers were paid by the bushel. Before 1939 the rate was 12d for two bushels; it then improved to 10d a bushel and steadily increased thereafter. A good picker, probably helped by children, could manage 25 bushels a day, but the average was 16 bushels .... on occasions the hop pickers did strike for more pay and this was negotiated by the gang leader who looked after the welfare of the gang. At the Lower House there could well have been 50 pickers from Dudley with perhaps 20 children. In addition there were probably another six local pickers. There were seven acres of hops on this particular farm and the labour needed during picking was about ten pickers to the acre.'

In a letter from Kingstanding we have more details of the social life of the hop pickers and of the gang leader, in this case a man.

'From the time I was born I was taken hop picking on the Hop Pickers special train from Snow Hill Station, Birmingham, every year up to the time my father died in 1939 ... we had to get up at 5.00 a.m. in the early hours to have a quick breakfast and then help my dad with the old tin trunk onto his tatting cart and push it from Aston to Snow Hill station where we got a trolley loaded with luggage, took it down the lift to the platform and took it to the train at the side platform; all the pickers were there with shouting and crying kids pushing onto the train. We had no corridors so we had to use a bucket in the carriage for a toilet and it was thrown out of the window while the train was moving. Our destination was Suckley, near Worcester, not far from Bromyard ... the hops were picked into cribs made of crossed poles with sacking. The hops were bushelled out of the cribs at a shilling a bushel in a bushel basket by the foreman … the hops were bagged into large sacks and carted to the kiln or oast house to dry. Our hands became black to the knuckles because of the sulphur sprayed on the hops and we had to use paraffin to clean it off. When we pulled the last wire we cheered and cribbed the young girls and covered them with dead bines. They were the best days of my life and I've loved the country ever since. I miss the ''crib up'' cry when a house was finished.

My father, Charles Gordon, was hired by the farmer Mr J. Field of Pewcroft Farm, Suckley to hire fifty pickers and their families for employment in September. He then received railway tickets by post to bring them to Suckley. My father then received one shilling per head as a bonus.

On the first day of picking my father went round the hop field to look at the size of the hops, if they were small he bargained for more money per bushel, if they were large the farmer bargained for less per bushel; in all the years we only had one strike for more money. There were two kinds of cribs, one family size and the other single size. We cut the bines on the bottom and pulled it down. Some hops were scattered on the floor and they had to be picked up before you moved your crib to another house or section to pick. Hop picking was a working holiday for the poor families of the cities, it was a healthy and profitable pastime in those days but there was a snag—my father was summoned and fined ten shillings for keeping us away from school for a month, but we, the children, enjoyed it…'

The Priest family at Frogend Farm, September 1950.

A letter came from a farm worker's son which emphasises the year round importance of the hop cultivation.

'.... Before the War my young life was spent among the hop fields of Hereford and Worcester. My earliest memories date back from 1926 until 1938 when I went into the forces but came back to Redditch to live after the War in 1946.

My father, a farm worker, had a comprehensive knowledge of hops and worked at all the various stages and, as such, so were the whole family. My earliest memories around 1926 were when hops were grown up poles, not strings... The season for us was not just the picking, it all started after the last hop was picked, the clearing and burning of the bines, the cuttings taken for new stock, the ploughing and fertilizing, the tying, the leafing, the spraying, so many vivid memories. Watching the growth until the appearance of the burrs to try to judge the quality of the crop. One thing which fascinated me a lot was the stringing in which my father was very proficient. I don't know how it is done these days but years ago it was by the use of a simple gadget on the end of a long pole which we called a monkey, and when it was finished looking across the hop field revealed a large diamond pattern. My earliest memories were of the square type rigid crib and the folding crib coming in about the mid Thirties. Where only one person or a couple were picking the crib was divided by a canvas partition for two families. Memories of the men called pole pullers, non existent toilet facilities, the vendors who visited the hop fields, the ice cream man with his motor cycle box sidecar attachment containing soft ice cream, the well known lady from Ledbury, Hannah Brace, with her basket of kippers, bloaters etc (who, incidentally, only died around the mid Seventies). Memories of the cold and frosty mornings, the fires built for the pickers to warm up their cans and kettles and make their crude barbecues of sausages, bacon and fish etc, bushelling time comments, the camp fires at night. The accommodation for the pickers provided by the farmers was in sheds, barns, stables and even pig-styes which had previously been thoroughly cleaned, whitewashed and clean straw provided for bedding ....'

Let us finish with an extract from a letter from Wordsley, near Stourbridge. The writer used to stay with 'Farmer Pudge, Frogend Farm, Bishops Frome, near Bromyard', and she writes:

'.... How funny our lives come in a circle because looking over the years as a child, I looked upon hop picking as a happy holiday time; in my teens and twenties I went through a stage of being ashamed to let my trendy friends know I even knew what hop picking was, and now in my forties I am here telling you about it with happy memories and pride at being part of a little bit of history....'

CHAPTER 5

Hymns, Health and Holidays

'Owing to the lengthy hop-picking it is found impossible to reopen the School (Whitbourne) until Monday October 7th. It is hoped that the parents will under no circumstances keep their children from School after that date.'

Bromyard Deanery Magazine, September 1901.

The many thousands of hop pickers who came into the countryside required a great deal of care and organisation, involving the local Churches, medical services, police and education authorities. But first the pickers had to be brought to the district and this was the responsibility of the railways and later, road transport. The *Bromyard News and Record* of 31 August 1905 has details of the arrival at Bromyard that week of the hop pickers' special trains, and lists the number of pickers, not counting the numerous children, destined for various farms in the district:

'Numbers on Monday, August 28

90	Mr W. Leake	(Ullingswick)
70	Mr J. Leake	(Morton Jeffries)
100	Mr E. Pudge	(Bishops Froome)
90	Mr Pudge	(Bishops Froome)
10	Mr J. Bayliss	(Ullingswick)
12	Mr J. Thomas	(Ullingswick)
20	Mr J. Davies	(Leominster)

Hop pickers' specials at Bromyard Station about 1910.

Tuesday August 29

50	Mr Green	(Bishops Froome)
14	Mr J. Hodges	(Stoke Lacy)
50	Mr Perry	(Much Cowarne)
25	Mr Pannier	(Much Cowarne)
40	Mr Ware	(Ullingswick)
60	Mr Parker	(Little Froome)
60	Mr W. Smith	(Mayfields)
50	Mr Dupper	(Stoke Lacy)

Wednesday August 30

40	Mr Birchley	(The Heath)
40	Mr Denney	(Hopton)
60	Mr G. A. Treasure	(Felton)
60	Mr Buckle	(The Hyde)
40	Mr Adney	(Much Cowarne)
16	Mr H. Taylor	(Avenbury)'

In addition, 1,000 hop pickers had been dropped at Knightwick and 400 at Suckley on the Wednesday, while two more specials were expected the following Sunday.

Hop pickers returning home with their trunks and bunches of hops. Stoke Edith Station around 1908.

By the '30s, motorcoaches were also being used for transporting pickers. Two of Gilbert Bowler's lorries from Bishops Frome, would fetch pickers from South Wales in the morning and from the Black Country in the afternoon. During the war, this was encouraged by the licensing authorities to relieve the pressure on the trains and buses. Two coaches and a lorry were needed to bring the pickers from the Cannock, Hednesford and Dudley area to the Parkers at Instone Court, Bishops Frome, and when they went home there would be a second luggage lorry paid for by the pickers and loaded with apples and other fruit.

HOP PICKERS' BARRACK.
MUCH COWARE HEREFS.

The local churches were most concerned about the welfare of the pickers, while at the same time taking the opportunity for a little evangelising. The *Bromyard Deanery Magazine* reported that five children had been baptised at Thornbury on 22 September 1901. The next year, at Much Cowarne and Moreton Jeffries, the vicar ran a hop pickers' mission with the help of Mr Collier, a cadet in the Church Army, at the end of which there were eight baptisms. Mr Collier who 'was most zealous in his work among the Pickers', had stayed with Colonel and Mrs Bourne at Cowarne Court. An entry for Stanford Bishop in 1905 reads:

> 'The Hop Pickers Mission last year was very encouraging, our visitors so appreciating what was then done for them, that probably most of the growers will be glad to join in doing something of the sort during the coming season. Even if we are not able to support a regular Missioner this year, it is very possible that we might have a series of lantern services, lectures upon domestic and sanitary subjects, etc.
>
> Addresses upon these matters will pass without attention in TOWN, but here in the country the pickers will welcome any evening recreation.
>
> Most of the people are very fond of singing and it is proposed to arrange some musical evenings for them. We are sure that the young people who helped in this way last year will do so again. And the

occasional tea or coffee is a great comfort after a day in the fields. The cost is not much, and if each grower and farmer would only contribute their "mite" towards the necessary outlay, the little refreshment might be given nearly every evening as an attraction to the meeting.'

Four pickers had died in the area and the prose of the period describes how:

'The painfully sudden death of a hop picker on the 5th inst. cast quite a gloom over the Parish. Abednego Richards had come from Wolverhampton with a party of hop pickers to work at the Hyde....'

Once a week, two Wesleyan Methodists, Miss Rose Moore the founder of the Boys' Own Brotherhood in Bromyard and Miss Kate Lewis, travelled out to Avenbury to hold a service in the hopyard at Munderfield Court. Miss Lewis played the harmonium which was brought from the house on a wagon. The pickers' children at Munderfield Court also attended Sunday School, along with some of their mothers who took advantage of the opportunity to learn to read and write. As already mentioned, on some farms members of the Salvation Army looked after the pickers.

In the '30s, a deaconess from Bristol with as many as six young girls preparing to be missionaries in Africa, would come to Bishops Frome to administer to the sick children. As everyone gathered round to sing and listen to her preaching, the gypsies used to take her under their wing, carry the organ and see that no one removed the light or pump from her bike.

During September there were no holidays or days off for doctors or nurses, and Philip Crosskey writes:

'Epidemics used to spread easily through the hop pickers' quarters which were crowded and rather primitive; as the weather could turn cold and wet, throat and chest infections were very common. A call to visit one family might result in seeing another half dozen families on the same farm and, with such difficult conditions, many had to go into hospital who would normally have been looked after at home. The maternity services in the area were provided by a devoted band of midwives who could tell many a story of babies delivered safely on straw palliasses by the light of hurricane lamps, and it was often said that the gypsies stayed in the area in order to avail themselves of these excellent facilities. At the Bean House, Cradley, their babies always seemed to arrive at hop-picking times, and Nurse Boucher, the district nurse, made sure of her £2 fee first in each case, as they were apt to depart at once after the child was born. Dr S. W. Russell, a general practitioner in Bromyard, was a noted obstetrician and was often reported to have spent nights on the straw in the hop pickers' quarters waiting for the final stages of labour and prepared to do fine midwifery under appalling conditions

Hop picking was also a busy time in the surgery, especially in the evenings and at weekends when the picking had finished, and the small cramped waiting room at Nunwell House would reek of the acrid smell of hops. Of course, there were all the incidental accidents that happened on farms when there was such intense activity in progress. Wasp stings were common amongst the children who used to walk around with a "piece", the jam spread all over the face and hands.

As a newcomer to the practice, it was not easy to grasp the pressing need to get the hop driers well enough to keep on with their work. They had tremendous loyalty to the farmer and the farm, and intense interest in proving their worth as driers by producing the best samples of hops. A lapse in the care of the drying process could be disastrous, so the drier and his health were the key to a successful hop picking.

Of course there were the skivers amongst the hop pickers who were on the sick list at home and wanted to continue drawing sick pay whilst earning money hop picking. Then there was the occasional patient who fell ill towards the end of hop picking and "needed" an ambulance to get home! But these were the few; the many kept well and the children always looked fitter and browner at the end of their month in the hopyards.

September is now much as any other month and the barracks and huts stand empty, mute reminders of all the noise, bustle and activity of the old hop picking days.'

The doctors were not the only ones to have their leave stopped. Constable Fred Harris was a well-known character in Bishops Frome who kept very firm control during the influx. He was a big, brawny man who made a point of knowing by name all the gypsies and many of the imported pickers, and could quickly apprehend any wrongdoers often dispensing instant justice on the spot in the shape of a heavy clout; Mrs Harris would have two extra constables billeted on her during the season. Other well-remembered names include P.C. Penry and 'Gunboat' Smith from Tarrington.

BARN & HOP PICKERS ACCOM^N AT LOWER COURT FARM BUCKLEY.

The start of the Autumn Term in hop-growing areas used to be delayed until after hop picking, but by 1952-3 a change in the dates of the school holidays to coincide with those for the rest of the country was causing a conflict of interests for parents of schoolchildren, both locally and in the Black Country: if the children were kept away from school their parents faced a fine in the magistrates' courts. The earlier start to the term, an increase in the numbers of children attending the Grammar School because of the 1944 Education Act, two cold, late hop-picking seasons and an active campaign by the Local Education Authority against children missing school for hop picking, engendered considerable debate at the time which is reflected in the following extracts from the *Bromyard News and Record.*

18 September 1952   The Hop Harvest

Hop farmers in the Bromyard district must be very well satisfied with the crops which are now being picked, and are in many cases above average.

Hop pickers had a good start to their holiday with pay but last week found the weather rather trying. It is most unusual to contend with North and East winds for a whole week and there must have been many very cold fingers especially amongst the very young.

The hop machines and the fines for children kept away from school seem to have had an effect on the number of outside pickers coming to the district. Local pickers have found employment either in picking or tending the machines.

18 December 1952 - A report of the National Farmers Union AGM:

Mr. N. D. O. Capper, branch delegate to the Hop Committee, told members that the committee was concerned that all schools were beginning the Autumn term at the same time, which was when hop picking commenced. They felt it was a very serious matter and hoped it would be possible to go back to the old system. Representatives of the Committee were to consult the Director of Education and his committee on the matter.

17 September 1953   Hop Picking and the Schools

Many schools in the hop-area are finding the number of absentees, since the term began on Tuesday, very high indeed. At Brockhampton, for instance, over 25 per cent were absent, while at Ashperton the percentage was still higher.

On Wednesday, Bromyard Senior School had 56 absent out of a total of 231. Many parents had sent for and filled in and returned forms due to taking their annual holidays from their employment for this fortnight. In some few cases these filled-in forms may have been meant for real holidays, but the majority undoubtedly were meant in order to go hop picking and take the children along.

The first question which therefore arises is whether hop picking possibly on the same farm as that on which the father is already employed, is "from my employment". The next is, if the mother signs the form as parent, is she on annual holiday if she does not leave home except to walk to and work in the hop yards?

If the answer to these two questions, or either of them, is "yes", then it seems that the filling in of the forms is a mere farce and a waste of paper, and that the best thing to do is to return to having the annual summer holiday in hop areas in late September and October as in most schools in previous years. If the answer is "no" then the parents should realise that they are in danger of prosecution.

It would be helpful if the Education Authorities would give an answer to the questions so the parents would know just where they stand.

It quite obviously is not fair on the school teachers to have to start a new year, with children beginning in new forms, when only half to three-quarters of them are present, and in a fortnight's time they will have to begin all over again on the others when they come back.

There is also bound to be a waste of public money in buses running to the schools with only a handful of children in them, or, as in the case of Fromes Hill to Ashperton last Tuesday morning with none being picked up at Fromes Hill.

Also, presumably, even if no dinners were wasted on the first day, the full canteen staffs had to be paid for cooking dinners for far fewer children than usual.

This matter is a serious one for all concerned, and it is essential that a satisfactory solution shall be worked out immediately to ensure that the winter term in 1954 begins with all children being present at their schools.

24 September 1953   Hop Picking and the Weather

The hop pickers in the Bromyard district have so far had little help from the weather, which has varied between a little sun, sudden storms, and wild winds.

The number of pickers has fallen considerably, due to the growing number of machines now in use, and also due to the healthy respect that sharp fines last year for keeping children away from school, engendered in the minds of many parents from the Birmingham and Dudley areas.

Where machines are used work has continued in all but the very worst weather, and another two or three weeks should see it all over.

8 October 1953 - A report of the previous week's Rural District Council meeting:

Inspection of Hop Pickers' Accommodation by Dudley Education Department.

The Clerk reported that he had written to the Education Department of the Dudley Council asking if a deputation had been visiting local farms to inspect the accommodation of hop pickers' children and stating the Council's disapproval of any such inspection without their knowledge.

This matter had been raised by the Surveyor in the Housing and Health Committee meeting, and the Medical Officer had objected strongly to such a visit.

In reply to his letter the Clerk said that they (the Dudley Council) regretted that the visit had taken place without the Council being notified. They had no intention of interfering with the Council's administration, but it has been the practice for a number of years for members of their Education Committee to visit farms and see how the children were accommodated. Apologies were made and it was stated that in future the Council should be told of proposed visits.

The end of an era was not to be delayed, and by 1960 employment at the local glove factory, in the school meals service and at the hospital had absorbed the nimble fingers and willing hands, and provided a more regular income for many married women. The children's education had become more important than the hop-picking money.

HOP TOKENS.

CHAPTER 6

A Farmer's Diary

'Here are four harvests, the hay; the corn; the hop and the cider.'

John Clarke, 1794.

The late Ted Holloway of Lower House, the Bull Ring and Hope House in Stanford Bishop, and Sevington in Acton Beauchamp, kept a series of day books covering the years 1951 to 1977. Not all the events listed below occurred in any one year, but an attempt has been made to show the working year on a mixed farm, where hops were only one of many enterprises, by condensing the twenty-seven year span of entries into twelve months.

January

Plant hop roots. Trimmed hopyard hedge. Lower House hops sampled. Repaint barn in top yard. To Rosemaund to buy 84 wire work posts. 6 tons of slag spread on bottom hopyard. Hopgrowers' meeting. Bought 36 hop poles. Snow and heavy drifting during night. Ditched landrover at Hawkins. Met Ministry man re kilns. Plough up hops. 6 tons of bones. Squaring up accounts from hop-picking.

February

Pegged out wirework. Ploughing finished except for hops. Plough down hops. Received hop valuations. Trimming inside hopyard hedge. Death of the King (1952), muck spreading. King's funeral, good weather. Muck hauling. Currant planting. Stocking hops. Winter washed currants. George had lorry to haul posts from Rosemaund, broke down on way home. Finished ploughing currants and started hops. Put artificial on hops. Fencing around bottom hopyard. Wages up to £12 8s. per week (1969).

March

New tractor. Ploughed down hops at Bull Ring, working on wirework. Started cutting hops. Put some K nitro on hops. Nitro chalk on currants. Beechams man called re currants. Throwing down and cutting hops. Wonderful weather. Sowing. Manure on currants and hops, spreader broken. Finished ploughing and cutting hops. Picked up a few cuttings. Planting hop roots. Started to spread shoddy. Poles came to all farms. Ernie wireworking. Cutting hop pegs.

April

Harrowed hops. Sprayed currants. Red Rum won Grand National. Planted currant cuttings. Spreading shoddy on hops. String arrived. Getting reversion out of currants. G. to London re hops. Stringing. Hop pegging. Planted oats in hopyard at Sevington. Muck from big shed to Bull Ring. Harrow currants. Mr D. and others here re hop-picking machine. Planted potatoes between currants.

George Holloway, Harry Brooks, Fred Anthony (stockman, busheller and dryer) and Ted Holloway about 1945.

May

Women hop tying. 3 Bromyard women bracing. Finished rotavating currants. All staff hop tying. Hop insurance man. See vicar of Bromyard re electricity in church. Cold all week, nothing growing, hops very backward. Finished hooking and stringing. Put phosphate on first hopyard. 3 Bromyard women doing hops second time. Sprayed currants.

June

Started moulding hops. Rolled and harrowed hops. Sheepshearing. Cold for whole week, bad for time of year nothing growing, frost damage everywhere. Spraying hops. Started mowing for hay. Blight very bad. All hops to have heads trained, found leaf spot. Burning hop bottoms. Working in currants. Sorting potatoes, mowing at Sevington. Bad blight sprayed hops. Finished tying hops second time and sprayed bases with tar oil. Potters' cattle been in hops. Started hopwashing. Bad thunderstorm Hope House hop kiln struck by lightning. Baled hay. Swarm of bees came. Powdered hops for nettle head (1961). Stripping hops. Mowed seeds, hoeing roots.

July

Hop training, very hot. Started to plough up old hopyard. 4 women cutting out downy mildew in hops. Started currant picking. 121 trays of currants. Whitewashing for arrival of hop pickers. Too hot to spray hops after 12 noon. Currant pickers strike for more money. Hop insurance man inspected hopyards.

Hope House - Jack Powell moulding the hops in June with a Cleatrac (Cleveland, USA tractor 1918-20).

Harrowing hops. Wages up to £30. 5s. (1975). Cultivating hops, found blight, all hops to be resprayed. Hop washing, hay making. 172 trays of currants. Baby lost, place in pandemonium, police involved, all had refreshments. Powdered hops with hormone. Washing hops, blight worse than expected. Mowing machine broken, baler also broken down. Hops not moving much.

August

Finish picking old currants. Started others. 253 trays. Sprayed potatoes. Currant pickers back home, working hops, plum picking. Sprayed hops for blight, remainder to currants. Sprayed hops found more blight than good. Put Bordeaux mixture on hops. Cutting corn and baling hay. 50 chips of plums to Hereford. Started hop-pickers' quarters. Gales all night and day, some hops badly affected. Cleaned hop kiln. Post in wire work broken, propped up temporarily. Blued hops. Following gale lots of strings down and cross wires. Hop-pickers arrived. Hope House, B. Cross putting sheets on barn.

September

Hop-picking good progress. Sulphured hops. Picking Goldings hot and windy. Fair first day at Hope House 144 sacks. Bagger broken, repaired bagger, bagged hops. Hops deteriorated from last Tuesday's rain. Every farmer a little worried. Beginning to understand machine (1961). Hops weighing light. Good weather,

Fred Anthony powdering at Lower House in the 1930s.

finished first hopyard light crop. Broke bagger again. Machine doing better. Very good hops from Sevington. Hops to Ledbury. Mushrooms. Sent 39 pockets to P. Pudge. Hops being very wet picked dirty. Bagger broke. Finished picking. Cutting bines. Started damson picking. Good week 4 kiln loads every day.

October

Finished drying 262 pockets. Drew money to pay hop-pickers. Finished burning bines. Moved hops to warehouse. Dismantled hop-picking machine. Pickers back to Dudley. Geo to Tenbury—hop prizes. Potatoes finished. Started apple picking. Finished thatching ricks (1954). Put 3 ton slag on hops. Geo showed hops again did well. Planting hop roots. Finished stubble ploughing. Planted wheat. Hope House hops sampled. Too wet to spray. Harvest supper at Parish Room. Muck spreading on hops. Ploughing up hops. Started getting up hop roots quite a big job but not so many as I thought, a few or more for sale.

November

Trimming hopyard hedge. Tractors all out of order. Muck on hops. Ploughing up hops. Bad wet weather. Got 500 hop roots ready for Newton Williams. Fetched 20 hop poles. Spread shoddy. To Worcester with hop roots.

December

Mucking hopyards. Topping hopyard hedge. Hop roots from R. Anthony. Redfern looking at elms with disease (1971). Finished mucking hops. Land wet. Watkins on wirework. Begin currant pruning. Hop valuation. Spray currants with tar oil, bad weather for job. Saw Watkins re hop poles. Foot and mouth at the Seed, Cradley, fetched 5 cattle in to feed from Jumpers Hole under license. Plough up hops.

Entries for December 31:

1954	Ploughing hops Bull Ring.
1958	A remarkable season, weather almost uncanny, records broken, shocking for harvest and hop-picking. Stock did well.
1959	No hunting for quite a time. Frost—distemper—then foot and mouth.
1962	Snowed in, nothing done beside stock. Men walked to work.
1964	Hops being sampled.
1965	Wages rose to £10.10.0.
1970	Wages up to £14.16.0.
1973	Except for frost taking currants a wonderful season. Hops in plenty; also corn, hay, etc. Very open autumn.
1977	A funny year. Plenty of most things. No currant buyers.

Bromyard Queen Nancy at the bottom of the Old Road, Bromyard, with a load of shoddy for the hopyards. The steam engine made by John Fowler of Leeds in 1909 was a common sight round Bromyard until 1934.

CHAPTER 7

Students and Shepherd's Pie

'Of all other dooings house keeping is cheefe.'

Thomas Tusser, 1524?-1580.

The establishment of the picking machine in the mid-1960s caused infinite regret to many people, but surely sighs of relief were heaved by farmers' wives and families. Life must be easier for them now, in the 1980s, when more depends on a well-regulated machine and less on unpredictable hungry human beings. However, for the high quality crops wanted by the brewers today, hops have to be harvested at the peak of their condition. This means working for the maximum number of hours during that time, and Gwenllian Paske of Upper Lyde, three miles north of Hereford, begins with sentiments remarkably familiar:

'September—once one is a hop farmer's wife that month will never seem the same again. For it is in September that hop picking happens—a hectic period of 2½-4 weeks.

On our farm a two-shift system was started recently and involves commencing at 6 a.m. and going on till 1 a.m. With a 19-hour day, it means that some workers need to start very early if on the 6 a.m. to 3.30 p.m. shift, and much later if on the second shift, 3.30 p.m. to 1 a.m. As all jobs are duplicated, except in the kiln, more workers are needed. There were not enough locally, so the solution has been to employ students. They are accommodated in caravans hired for the "picking". Our hop farm is not situated, as some farms are, very near to a catering pub for these students—about twenty—to have a pub lunch or any meals. A possible option could have been a shop offering various provisions, but we decided after all to provide all meals.

The thought of providing the students' meals, meals for the three kiln men and not forgetting the family, did seem overwhelming at first. Panic—but then an important part of the hop farmer's wife's make-up, placidness and adaptability, were drawn on. A timetable was the first item to be arranged. Gradually everything then fell into place, type of meal, extra plates and cutlery needed, etc., etc. How fortunate that the School Meals Service was drastically cut back just then!

Preparations for hop picking in September begin early in the year in springtime—the work force, who is available? For the students, advertisements are placed in student magazines or notices are sent to maybe an agricultural college to be pinned on their notice board for holiday jobs. You just sit back then and hope that the short time with good rates of pay will attract.

Nearer September detailed planning goes on. The supplier of the caravans, the milkman for extra milk, are notified, and then of course there is the menu. Actually, these menus and notes if safely kept reduce preparation and serve as

Gwen Paske serving yet another meal at Upper Lyde in 1987.

guide-lines for each year. During August the butcher is contacted for meat to be cut up into joints for roasting and boiling, other meat into pieces for casseroles and meat pies, and mince for shepherd's pies. All of this goes into the freezer, at least one hopes it will. Also into the freezer in August go fruit cakes and buns, and pastry for topping the popular chicken and mushroom or fruit pies.

During the week prior to hop picking is the "big shop" and this hopefully includes enough of all dry goods to take one through the period. Back home with these goods and then the dairy is full and cupboards are bursting; the cellar has never been used like this since the days before fridges. It must be remembered that during hop picking there is only minimum time for shopping.

At last, the "day before" arrives, the day for all the last-minute jobs that have been put off, e.g. is the First Aid Box complete? And in the late afternoon and evening the students should arrive. Note, I use "should arrive" as thoughts cross your mind, did they receive the information sheet sent out three weeks earlier? Perhaps they have decided not to come after all, the girlfriend wants Tim to go elsewhere, and then the telephone rings, "I am at Hereford Station, can someone come and meet me?" Soon after, a bright coloured jalopy arrives and I relax once again, there will be some workers! At last to bed, my husband and I each with an alarm clock!

The day of the start, and 5.15 a.m. the alarm goes off. The early shift are woken up, breakfast smells come from the welcoming warm kitchen and the first

<u>Mr. and Mrs. H.N. Paske, Upper Lyde, Hereford, HR4 8AE</u>
Telephone – Hereford 760220

Leave Hereford on A49 Leominster/Shrewsbury Road. Pass Lyde Church on your right after approximately 3 miles and take the next left turn by telephone box (before Greenhous' Garage). Proceed up lane ½ mile (beware of bends) and first farmhouse on your right is Upper Lyde.

Arrive previous day afternoon/evening.

<u>Hoppicking begins</u>   at 6.00 a.m.(if possible)
Confirmation of date will be given in August.

Please bring :-   Sleeping Bag
                    Wellington Boots
                    Alarum Clock
                    Clothes for WET and COLD Weather
                    Thermos Flask

Meals are provided and there are facilities (kettle, toaster, boiling ring) for extra snacks.

<u>AT WEEKENDS</u> – <u>On Saturdays</u>   Light lunch for <u>early shift workers only</u>
                                Cereal and toast available for 2nd Shift.

            <u>On Sundays</u>   Breakfast of cereal and toast available

<u>1st Shift:</u>   <u>2nd Shift:</u>

5.30 a.m. Breakfast   No work on Saturdays
6.00 a.m. – 9.00 a.m. Work   Breakfast – help yourself
9.00 a.m. – 9.30 a.m. Break   1.00 Dinner
          (Flask & Biscuits)   3.30 p.m. – 7.00 p.m. Work
9.30 a.m. – 12 noon   Work   7.00 p.m. – 8.00 p.m. Meal
12 noon   – 1.00 p.m. Dinner   8.00 p.m. – 10.30 p.m. Work
1.00 p.m. – 3.30 p.m. Work   10.30 p.m. – 11.00 p.m. Break
3.30 p.m. – Tea (1st shift only)   (Flask and Biscuits)
                                      11.00 p.m. – 1.00 a.m. Work
Saturday – work only until
           approximately 12 noon

Wages £.......... per hour.   National Insurances contributions
                             will be deducted.

£......... per day (5 days per week) will be deducted for keep.

P.A.Y.E. is not deducted from genuine students

Information sheet for hop pickers.

pot of tea of the day is made. Not much conversation is needed at this time, just instructions! The first breakfast is over, the students, quite likely dressed in warm clothes, and the hopyard gang with their flasks, climb onto trolleys and are off to gather the first bines. Other workers go to the machine to work there, and the "rattlings" from the machine start up as the motors are switched on and the various tracks go into motion.

For me, there is such relief to have reached this stage, to have started "hopping". Obviously, I have to have extra help in the house for preparation of vegetables (the saucepan for potatoes is so large that it seems the bottom will never be covered), telephone calls and messages (although the cordless telephone helps considerably here), some cleaning that must be done regularly (most important in washing and toilet places) and of course the dishwasher can't take all the washing up.

Home nursing is needed at times, if only for dealing with a nasty cut that may mean a stitch at the local hospital.

Mealtimes keep coming and with an element of luck on your side everyone seems satisfied. Gradually, one learns the likes and dislikes. How nice it is to remember the person's name when passing them their meal—but that is being hopeful in the first days! Then one finds that in the dairy there is room to move groceries around, the freezer will shut properly, there is only one pack of toilet paper left!

At last, when cutlery, plates, etc., are packed away, chairs are really clean, one contemplates rather wearily, that's enough for this year, next year will come round soon enough!'

Load of hops in front of the old kilns at Upper Lyde with a cowl showing above the pockets and the old greenstage (space for stacking green sacks) at the rear.

CHAPTER 8

Hop Kilns

'Some skilfullie drieth their hops on a kell,
   and some on a soller, oft turning them well.
Kell dried will abide, foule weather or faire,
   where drieng and lieng in loft doo dispaire.'
                              Thomas Tusser, 1524?-1580.

Hops must be carefully dried and special buildings have been developed for this purpose; in some areas these are called oasthouses, but in Herefordshire they are known as hop kilns. An early method of drying was to spread the hops on an upper floor or in an attic and allow them to dry naturally. In his book, *A Perfite Platforme of a Hoppe Garden* published in 1574, Reynolde Scot describes such a method: 'If you have no Oast dry them in a loft open to the air as maybe lay them not above half a foot thick and turn them once a day at the least, by the space of two or three weeks sweep them up into a corner let them lay for as long more.' Some local growers without kilns were using Scot's method as late as the 19th century, while others took their hops to be dried by their larger neighbours; eventually all hop growers built their own kilns. In 1842, for example, there were 23 farms in Stoke Lacy growing hops, of which at least 14 are known to have had kilns or to have built them later. Of the 10 kilns that survive, one is in use and most of the others are now falling into decay.

There have been many types of kilns but all have used the same principle of rising hot air to dry the crop. A slatted wooden floor, 8 to 10 feet above a smokeless fire, is covered with a woven horsehair cloth on which the green hops are spread in a thin layer. The 17th-century version used in Herefordshire was a small brick fireplace about 3 feet square, with an inverted lath and plaster cone above it leading the hot air up to the drying floor above, some 8 feet square. By the 18th century, brick had replaced the lath and plaster cone and small ventilators were fixed on the ridge of the roof for the hot air to escape. These early kilns were housed in a low, two-storey, ridge roof building, usually joined to the house with access between the house and the kiln, both upstairs and downstairs. A few of these 17th and 18th century kilns still exist in the district. The round brick kiln, with a tall tapering roof topped by a cowl that can swing with the wind, was in use by the 1830s. Forty years later, these had changed to a square plan which was easier to use. These in turn became larger, with full-length ridge ventilators in place of the cowl. The height of these kilns increased the draught and airflow through the hops, producing a better sample. In order to increase the draught still further, some kilns were built very high indeed.

Another method that was tried was to insert a second drying floor, above an existing floor, on which the green hops were partly dried before being transferred to the lower floor for the drying to be completed. In theory this should have meant that one could dry double the weight of hops in one kiln with no increase in fuel consumption. Although a popular method today, at that time, in practice, it was

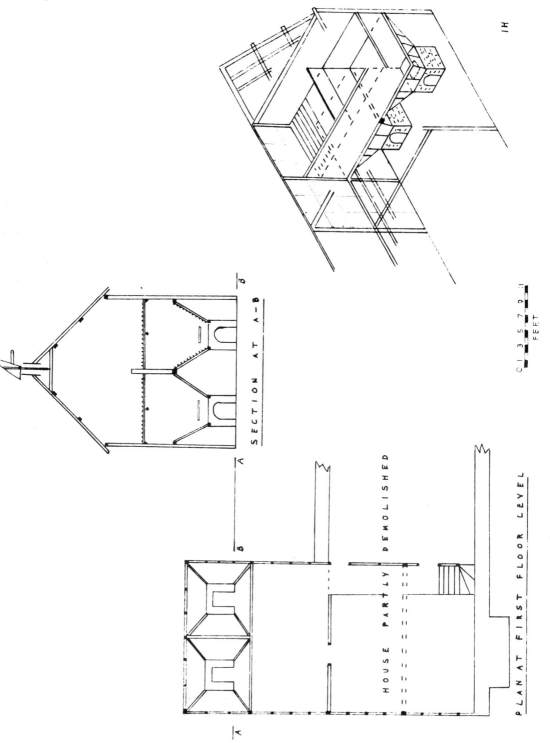

Details of early 18th-century lath and plaster hop kilns in Whitbourne.

SECTION AT A–B

PLAN AT FIRST FLOOR LEVEL

HOUSE PARTLY DEMOLISHED

C 1 3 5 7 9 11
FEET

Linton Brook around 1910. The service-wing contained the hop-drying kilns, and the louvres for the hot air to escape can be seen on the ridge of the roof.

found that one did not save the fuel expected and the labour costs were more than doubled. A few of these early double-decker kilns were constructed in Herefordshire, but as far as is known none in the Bromyard district.

One of the essential elements in hop processing is the need for fuel for their drying, and early kilns were heated by charcoal or hardwood, and later coal. A particularly suitable coal was obtainable from the south-west flanks of the Wyre Forest coalfield in the Worcester/Shropshire borderlands. Here, outcrops of two series of coal measures occur: (i) the 'Productive Coal Measures', and (ii) the 'Upper Coal Measure'—also known as 'sweet' and 'sulphur' coal respectively. These sulphuric upper coal measures were extensively mined in the west and south of the coalfield at such pits as Bayton, Mamble, Hollins and Pensax. This fuel gave off sulphur when burned and was favoured for hop drying as it improved the colour of the hops. Not far away, the Darby family discovered the process of converting coal into a form of coke in the early 18th century; there is a record that in 1717 'chard coal' was to be delivered annually to the vicar of Lindridge some twelve miles north of Bromyard, and it was probably in use locally soon afterwards. Through the 19th century and until just before the First World War, hop growers in the Bromyard district hauled bulky loads of coke (known as charks) from Pensax and Mamble for their kilns. With teams of horses and wagons the return journey of up to 60 miles took two days across quite challenging terrain and was accomplished with much relief and refreshment. Even today (1988), fifteen years after the closure of the last pit, there is still evidence of the mine-workings. With the coming of the railways, another smokeless fuel, anthracite, had become available from South Wales, and by 1900 this was also fuelling steam engines used to drive fans which forced air through the kilns. (See chapter 11 for more recent developments in hop drying.)

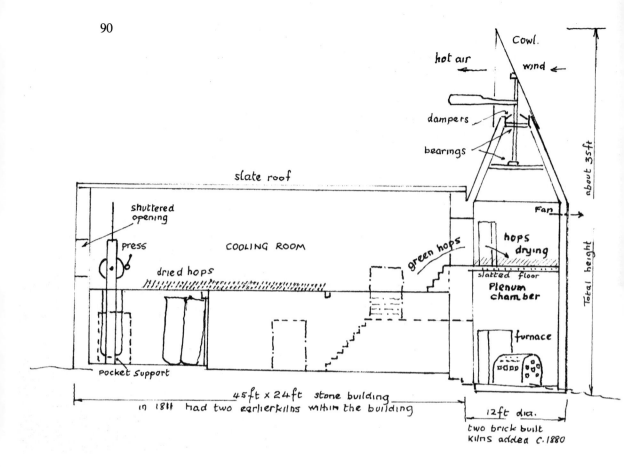

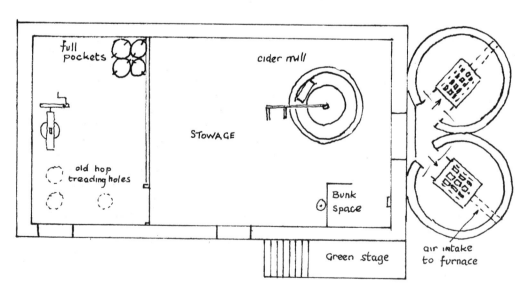

A small hop-drying unit at Little Cowarne Court in use until 1959.

LITTLE COWARNE COURT HOP KILNS

The original 16th or 17-century stone building, known as the Mill after the cider mill, is a good example of the way farm buildings have been adapted over the years. The west end has a fine fireplace and may have been the original farmhouse with a granary above. The 18th-century hop drying unit probably consisted of a pair of kilns against the east end of the building in the area now taken up by the cider mill, and the granary was also used as a hop room for cooling and bagging. The old hop treading holes have been boarded over and nowadays traces can only be detected from below. The brick hop kilns of c1880 are unusual in having brick cones instead of the more customary slate or tile hung roofs of Herefordshire. The bricks were baked on the farm by Thomas Fletcher of Rose Cottage, Little Cowarne; building round kilns would have been no problem for a bricklayer used to sinking brick-lined wells. The cones were waterproofed with pitch and the pointed cowls protected by lead tips. An extractor fan was added to improve the draught - see illustration above left with William Pearson standing beside its engine in 1956. The furnace in its later form was fired with anthracite and never converted to oil fuel; similarly, the hand-driven press was never converted to power. The bunk space was for the drier who had to live on the job during hop picking.

The Farm, Brockhampton, about 1963. Again, the conical tops to the kilns are brick. This flat-topped cowl clearly illustrates the many tapered strips of wood used in its construction.

Elmores End, Whitbourne, *c*1911, with twin cowls atop a slate-roofed rectangular brick kiln.

quare kiln with a ridge ventilator at Kidley, Acton Beauchamp, built by anford of Suckley in 1900.

A similar kiln with sacks of hops on the green-stage waiting to be dried.

In the days of the anthracite fires the hop driers were very skilled and trusted men. The fires had to be kept at an even red glow *all* the time which entailed stoking probably every half-hour night and day. There were thermometers to show the temperature of each kiln and these had to be watched carefully for any change. The head drier also had to know the exact time to unload the hops by feel, smell and general condition. As it was a twenty-four hour job there were usually at least two driers to take it in turns to tend the fires, but both were needed for unloading the kiln during the night as this entailed moving a large volume of hops. Extra labour was often available during the day for loading, when the head drier would be in charge and rake the hops to the required depth on the kiln floor, while the other men brought greensacks on their backs and emptied them where directed.

The driers had their own rooms for resting and had their short sleeps on a palliasse stuffed with straw. When on duty they had to keep awake, the drier in charge at Cradley Hall Farm in the early '30s, Sidney Box, a well-known local man of strong radical opinions, kept a bottle hanging from the ceiling in the kiln so that if he nodded off he knocked himself against it and woke up. Others chose to sit in a wheelbarrow when on duty (handles on the ground) so that if they dropped off to sleep the wheelbarrow would tip and they would wake up. The driers' room was often quite a social centre in the evenings with locals calling in for a chat and to hear how the picking was progressing, bringing news from other farms and general gossip. A game of darts was the popular pastime on these occasions and some visitors would stay on to help with changing the kilns. The local policemen also used to come round from time to time. In most cases the driers' week finished in the early hours of Sunday morning when they went home and then had to be on duty again mid-day on Monday.

Robert Maund stacks the greenstage at Panks Bridge Farm in 1968.

Walter Dew stoking the kiln fire at Upper Lyde. The horseshoe is for lighting the sulphur (see page 150).

Walter Dew levelling hops - note the unguarded belt for the extractor fan in the background.

A lifter hair in a kiln at Stanford Court. The early hairs were permanently fastened down and the hops pushed out with a hop shovel.

The next stage: Richard Potter removes the hops from the kiln.

The hops in a pile for the moisture to be redistributed before being bagged.

After the hops have been dried they have to be tightly packed into large, strong, jute sacks or pockets, each pocket measuring 6 feet by 3 feet and holding about 1½ cwt of hops when full. The hops are compressed in this manner partly for transport, but mainly for storage as when tightly packed they will keep for long periods. The method of packing the hops into the pockets remained the same in many places until the late 19th century. A round bagging or treading hole, of which many local examples still exist, was cut in the upper floor of a hop room or farmhouse and a hoop slightly larger than the hole was sewn in the mouth of the pocket, which was then passed down through the hole and suspended by the hoop. In later years, the open end of the pocket was turned over the hoop which then fitted onto a flange surrounding the bagging hole. A telling description of the operation occurs in E. J. Lance's *The Hop Farmer* published in 1838:

> 'The hops are tramped into these bags by a man, while a boy supplies him from a basket and it will take 3 to 4 hours to tramp each bag, and to tramp 4 bags @ 9d is a very good day's work for a man. In treading the man becomes covered in yellow dust; it nearly chokes the man and he must be supplied with beer to keep his throat clear.'

In Herefordshire, the drink could also have been cider or perry, but the job was just as dusty for most local treading holes were placed near a door to gain as much light and air as possible. After the pocket was full, the hoop was removed and the pocket lowered to the floor below where it was sewn up and weighed, the weight being stencilled on the side.

In the first half of the 19th century the hop press had been invented, a mechanical device to pack hops into a pocket without the need for a man to go down into it. It contained a plunger that could be rammed into the pocket by multiple gearing, then withdrawn for more hops to be added and forced down again and again until the pocket was full. The early hop presses were hand-operated but today they have all been converted to power.

Operating a press by hand and using a 'scuppet' to push the hops. The open end-flaps of the pocket were pulled over a ring, similar to the one on the wall, before the pocket was lowered into the bagging hole.

Richard Potter stands beside a full pocket suspended below the press. Three generations of Gladys Draper's family have helped with the hops at Stanford Court, and before the press was installed her grandmother, Mrs Hill of Shobdon Cottage, not only worked on hop tying and picking but trod hops there as well.

Pockets ready to go to the warehouse.

Kiln tools at Stanford Court: two square wooden shovels or scuppets, with an older round-headed one on the right; a wide rake; and a wooden fork with extra tines.

Also in the picture are two balls of hop string; a bundle of hop pegs; a pole-puller's pole; and an old stencil for marking the pockets.

Pockets of dried hops being loaded at Felton Court in 1933. Loading pockets on to lorries was a skilled operation, for the loads were of five layers and very high. In spite of being so unwieldy, the pockets were usually loaded with the name of the grower and farm inside to prevent prying eyes assessing how much a farm was producing by the number on the pocket. But if a farmer had a heavy crop and consequently high numbers, he might ask for the name and numbers to be loaded outwards! Some rows of the load had an overhanging end-pocket known as 'the slinger', which was unsupported and held only by the ropes running between the other layers of pockets.

Hop driers and their tools outside a Madley kiln in 1901: wooden scuppets, a pan of roll sulphur, perhaps charks in the sieve, a pocket still with its sack hooks and the bagger with his strings for sewing it up, while the bowler-hatted farmer records the weight of his crop.

FETCHING THE CHARKS

Nowadays, with oil delivered by road tanker, fuel is no longer the problem that it used to be when charks had to be hauled by the farmer from a colliery. In 1908, the 'boy' accompanying the last wagon loads of charks hauled from Mamble Colliery to Gold Hill Farm, Bosbury, was Inett Homes's father, and Inett compiled the following account of the journey from the description his father gave him fifty years ago:

'In the local hop growers calendar one of the major events was fetching the charks, used to dry the hops, from the colliery at Pensax. Two wagons and ten or twelve horses could only just make the twenty mile journey from Bosbury to Mamble and back in two days. Two wagons with eight horses could make the journey but it took longer, as on the many steep hills two trace horses had to be taken back down the hill to help the second wagon up. The charks were very light and so that the wagons could haul a large load of four tons or more, what were known as chark boards were put on the top of the wagon to raise the sides 4-5 feet. They were built like the sides of a boat and curved outwards so that the accommodation was larger at the top than at the bottom. In some places they were known as charky boards, but certainly round the Bosbury area they were called chark boards.

Prior to the event, wagons and chark boards were overhauled and checked for any damage, axles greased, lamps provided, harness cleaned and checked, and brasses polished. The horses would be in first-class condition and shod with new shoes all round, and a spare set carried in the tool box. In the wagons were placed a cask of cider for the colliery manager, two casks for the colliers, a ham for the manager and a side of bacon for the colliers. Without these it was not possible to get the wagons loaded on the first evening. Also in the wagons were two days' food for the horses, and two days' food and drink for the wagoners and carters.

As these wagons carried food and drink it was common for them to be waylaid and robbed on the journey. For this reason the 'boy' was put in the wagon and given an iron bar with instructions to hit any hands or heads that came in sight over the top.

On the morning of departure, the horses were cleaned, watered and fed long before dawn, and everyone adjourned to the kitchen for a huge breakfast. At the crack of dawn the convoy set off on the long, hard journey, stopping at intervals to water the horses, and at the Baiting House, Upper Sapey, for bait or elevenses. With luck they arrived at the colliery by the late afternoon and were loaded up that evening.

On the High Lane there were two ambushes and, but for the help of his dog in the wagon with him, Father thought they would have been overpowered and robbed.

The night was spent under the wagons and at dawn next morning they started back home, on the harder and more dangerous part of the journey. These wagons, which when loaded weighed nearly four tons, were equipped with double shafts so that there were two shaft horses side by side and four trace horses in front. There were no brakes and the two shaft horses had to hold the wagon back on hills. On steep hills a heavy cast-iron slipper was placed under one rear wheel and the wheel tied. It then slid along the road on the slipper. At the bottom of the hill the slipper would be too hot to handle but it had to be picked up and hung on the hook provided. To prevent the wagons running backwards if stopped on a hill, a wood and metal bowler trailed along behind a wheel and on a jerk of its chain would squat the wheel.

The journey home was uneventful except for a gang of wives complaining that their husbands were off work because of injuries received in fights. A few coins and a lump of bacon were thrown on the road and the women started fighting amongst themselves as to who was going to get the biggest piece.

At Bishops Frome the wagons were met by someone who galloped off home with the news that they were safely down Summerpool Hill. They arrived at Gold Hill at dusk, tired but happy that they were safely back. The horses were watered and fed and everyone entered the kitchen for a huge supper. If, as was often the case, it was a joint expedition between two or more growers, one usually provided the departure breakfast and the other the arrival supper.'

1¼" diameter hop token. Brass.

CHAPTER 9

The Hop Grower's Year

'The hop joyeth in a fat and fruitful ground: also it groweth among briers and thornes about the borders of fields, I meane the wilde kind.'
John Gerard, 1545-1612.

Since the Second World War the methods and productivity of British agriculture have probably altered and improved more than during any equivalent time span, and in the following calendars Harry Paske explains the differences that have occurred in hop growing. The system described before 1950 is as he remembers it at Little Froome. Hop growing was given up there in 1964 so he has described his own system at Upper Lyde for the present day.

The methods are peculiar to the periods and to the individual farms. No two hop growers ever had the same ideas or did things in the same way, and no two hop growers ever will, but the changes depicted are generally representative of the whole industry.

BEFORE MACHINE PICKING
(Pre 1950)

October

After hop picking, the bines, many of which would not have been severed, would be cut back to a few inches and tumped into alternate rows until dry enough to burn. This left the other rows free for loads of farmyard manure to be tipped into heaps for spreading when the bines were burnt.

November

After the FYM was spread the soil was ploughed up to the hops from the middle of the rows. This exposed the furrows to the frost, helping to create a tilth for next season and also, if the yard was suitably situated, helping rain to run off.

Ground for new yards was ploughed, cultivated level and the positions for new plants marked out with ground pegs.

MACHINE PICKING
(1985-6)

October

Earlier picking and the cutting of the bines for harvest, means we no longer rush in to cut off the remnants of the bines, but leave them on an extra month, so that the few remaining leaves can provide a certain amount of sustenance for the future. Ground pegs unprotected by the soil with which we used to smother the weeds, will need straightening and replacing, so as not to hinder cutting next month. We no longer use farmyard manure.

Frequent use of tractors produces 'no-go' areas for roots and a subsoiler is drawn through the ground just inside the wheelmarks to shatter the offending barrier. The high hedges are trimmed.

Diseased and surplus hops are grubbed with a tool originally designed by CWS Farms to lift their rhubarb stocks.

November

All surface hop growth has usually died off by the end of the second week and we are free to cut off the remnants of bine to ground level, ready for tumping up and burning when dry enough. Now that the crop is dormant it is safe to spray herbicides. Often, however, conditions are not good enough until March or April.

Areas for planting are ploughed if necessary and prepared with a power-driven harrow with reciprocating tines ready for marking out with ground pegs.

Burning bine.

December

Poles and wirework were checked and repairs and renewals made where necessary.

If new hop setts were not available from home-grown cuttings, they were bought privately or at Ledbury Hop Root Sale in November, and planted out when soil conditions were suitable.

January

New wirework was erected over the newly planted setts. Hedges were trimmed with hedgebills using ladders or standing on trailers where necessary. Ditches were cleaned and broken drains repaired. Prunings from the apple orchards were hauled to a convenient position to be available for hop pickers to collect for firewood in September.

December

Repairs and renewals are carried out to the wirework. The hop-picking machine is serviced by skilled fitters.

Hop roots certified virus free are planted out.

January

Wirework is erected over young hops. If the land has only been fallowed or rested from hops for two years, the wirework will not have been removed and only the installation of internal poles to support the wire will be necessary. Ditches are cleaned and drainage faults corrected. Yards are walked and dead stocks replaced.

Watkins and Griffiths also trim the high hedges surrounding the yards with a rotating flail hedge trimmer. This job we dare not do when the crop is growing. The anchor wires supporting the wirework tend to be hidden by leaves in the summer, and it is much too easy to accidentally sever a wire when it is under the tension of the weight of the crop, and a considerable collapse could then take place.

Trimming a hopyard hedge.

February

Wireworking was finished off, and top-hooks fixed to the parallel wires by operators using a long, pruner-like tool.

The ground is usually at its wettest during this month, but if conditions were unusually good a start could be made with spring operations.

March

The soil was ploughed from the hops back to the middle of the rows. Then the throwing down and cutting was done. Soil between the plants was removed by handwork with kerfs or three-pronged Canterbury hoes. The hops were then cut back to the crown by men with cranked cutting hooks. Good, healthy, strong cuttings would be selected from the debris for planting in a nursery for use as replacements the following year or even for gapping up in the current year. Damaged pegs were straightened or replaced. Except for the bigger growers, most farmers kept enough men to manage these jobs without casual labour at that time of year.

The first dressings of artificial fertilizer were applied if possible.

February

Wirework and top-hook replacement is completed.

The increased area of hops and decreased labour force make it necessary to start stringing hops this month or more casual labour will have to be employed in April. Under the old system of cultivating, the stringing could not go ahead anyway until the ploughing, throwing down and cutting had been done, so that the ground pegs were uncovered and could be put right to take the string.

March

As no cultivating work is to be done, when conditions are dry enough it is possible to catch up with any weed control spraying left over from the autumn. This needs to be done as soon as practicable so that unfolding leaves are not damaged.

Phosphate and potash fertilizer will be spread if the opportunity arises.

Martin Hewitt pegging at Panks Bridge Farm, Much Cowarne, in 1968. Graeham Davies stringing in the background.

Charlie Phillips stringing the Front Hopyard at Little Froome in the early 1950s. The string is carried in the bag and guided from peg to hook by the 'monkey', a long rod with a tube attached to one end.

Bracing the strings by tying them together with cut lengths of binder twine is no longer economic unless rows are so narrow that snagging from implements occurs.

April

The ground was cultivated when conditions were suitable, to level it off, as much as to kill weeds. Plants that had died were dug out and replaced.

Stringing had to be done in good time, as plants that were growing across the ground when they should be climbing the strings were very difficult to tie late and would be very slow to grow anyway. Regular labour would do the job on a piecework basis. Old Jim Walton had done the job for so many years that even when he could no longer see the top-hooks he was able to have a very creditable go at it.

Women did the next job—bracing the hop strings together with binder twine. This prevented them hanging loosely into the alleys to be snagged by traffic. At Little Froome a regular gang of up to a dozen women under the control of Elsie Bridgewater from the Ballhurst used to start the season with this job, following on with hop tying by the end of the month. For this the best shoots, not necessarily the strongest

April

A fungicide against mould is sprayed at least twice.

Stringing will be finished, the strings no longer being braced together, except at the end of the rows where it is necessary to prevent snagging by tractors when turning in.

Tying starts sometime after the 20th of the month. Here again the rules have been altered. The hop tiers' instructions are to see that at least three bines are furnished to each string. On no account are surplus bines to be removed unless there is no other way of furnishing the adjacent string with the right quantity. The basal growth is not to be removed and no time to be wasted by treading down unwanted bines.

Ground from which hops were grubbed last October and November will be cultivated as time and weather allow to keep free of weeds, and also to prepare a tilth ready for when the soil is warm enough in June or July to be injected with a soil sterilant.

April (cont)

and coarsest or those produced from long runners which tended to kink off later on, were trained clockwise round the string. The unwanted bines were ripped out by hand leaving two to grow up each string or perhaps two up one and three up the other in case one happened to perish.

May

The tying gang would go over a second time to attend to the weaker shoots and correct any bines that had heads entangled with each other, or which were climbing the wrong strings. Spiky heads infected with downy mildew would be picked and burnt, and Bordeaux powder applied as a preventive.

Cultivation and rolling continued as necessary to remove weeds, level the ground and create tilth.

A second dressing of fertilizer was applied.

May

The gang of five or six hop tiers will go twice round our forty acres and then two people will be sufficient to reposition any heads that stray from their predestined path, unless a period of quick growth is accompanied by strong gales which cause a great deal of havoc.

Clear polythene tubes, three to four foot long, are slipped over weak hops before the first defoliant spray of diluted tar oil is applied to kill off unwanted bottom growth.

Nettles and couch grass must be sprayed with a knapsack sprayer, and docks dug out by hand.

According to the soil analysis more phosphate or potash fertilizer may be applied. The first dressing of nitrogen will go on this month.

Fungicides will be sprayed at fortnightly intervals for the rest of the season.

Perry Pudge operating the hop-powdering machine that he developed to mount on a Fordson tractor in the early 1920s.

Hops being sprayed against aphid. Note the driver is wearing full protective clothing.

June

The tying gang returned to leaf the hops.

Hop damson aphid always appeared in June when the populations became too dense on the damson and blackthorn and had to migrate to the hop. Sprays or 4% nicotine dust were used. Hops were still walked and treated against downy and powdery mildews. By the middle of June, hops were expected to reach the top wire—it was then only 12 feet high—and the last nitrogen was applied (any later and there was a danger of hops being devalued for being too green).

Cultivations were carried out with scuffles, spring tines or discs, not only to kill weeds but to create a good depth of mould or tilth that was then ploughed over the base of the hops to smother weeds and encourage basal swelling to form good, strong cuttings.

At Little Froome any spare time from other farm duties in June was occupied by riding in a horse-drawn cart down the rows correcting heads that had fallen back from the strings because of the wind or other causes. In good growing weather a bine might grow a foot in twenty-four hours and a sudden change to windy weather could cause it to fall back before it had time to develop a grip on the string.

July

Cultivations were continued to suppress weeds. Aphids had to be destroyed at least once in the month and fungicides were included in the spray mix. Red spider was no problem because the systemic insecticides then in use were also extremely efficient acaricides. If downy mildew was still a problem the spike had to be removed, because if downy was not got rid of by the middle of the month there was trouble as it could destroy the developing burr (flower). If mould was still present the tying gang would have to return to strip off any regrowth of leaves on the lower bine.

Plants with the virus diseases nettlehead or mosaic were dug out, together with adjacent stocks in order to remove latent infection.

June

Because hop aphid usually appears during the first week of June, a measured dose of cytrolane spray is applied to each stock electronically. The tractor driver has to press the button 62,320 times so his thumb gets a little sore!

The last nitrogen will probably be applied, but if slow growth continues it may be put on as late as July, now that green hop samples are not frowned on as they used to be.

Hop heads are now out of reach from the ground, unless the workers are able to use forked sticks to control the recalcitrants by catching the heads and twisting them round the string. Unfortunately most people have insufficient co-ordination to do this without breaking off many of the heads, and if we are in real trouble with displacement a tractor fitted with a platform is used so the operation can be done by hand.

This month we take delivery of the diesel fuel used for drying. Progressive wilt starts to appear on infected farms from July onwards and tankers travelling from farm to farm in hop picking will be driving over the same paths as any wilted hops that may be coming in to the picking machines and then going on to the picking areas of non-infected farms. The risk of wilt transference in this way must be extremely great, particularly on farms where storage is such that deliveries may have to be made as often as twice a week during picking.

Fallowed soil will be injected with a sterilant.

July

The crop will have reached the top wire by the beginning of July and will start coming into burr about the middle of the month. Males are in a ratio of 1:200 and wind is the pollinating agent. Hops will develop from the burr without pollination but the crop won't be so heavy.

Fallen bines need restringing frequently, to prevent damage by hopyard traffic.

Red spider mite must be watched for in hot, dry periods.

From now on yards must be systematically and thoroughly walked at least once every week so that every single plant has been seen, and if

August

It was still important to clear up the weeds because of the hop pickers in September. Fat hen was remarkably uncomfortable to walk through when wet, even if one was properly dressed for the occasion, and the annual nettle (*urtica urens*) which seems to be more common in hopyards than anywhere else in this part of the country, although only half the size of the common stoloniferous variety has at least twice the stinging power.

Fungicidal dust was blown on the crop if necessary, but if a late fly-in of aphids occurred a complete spray mix was applied by the Three Counties Sprayers.

Preparations for hop picking began. Cribs were brought out of storage, torn cloths sewn up and broken timbers repaired. The kilns were cleared of all potatoes, fruit, corn, small dead animals and lost tools that had accumulated over the year. If the heating pipes hadn't been cleaned (and they usually hadn't), they had to be attended to. It was particularly important to clean the outside chimneys—one had exploded at Little Froome due to a dead owl being jammed in a bend. The kiln equipment—motors, fans, baggers, were all checked and lubricated. Greensacks and kiln hairs were repaired and the hop pockets obtained. Clean straw was stuffed into greensacks to make beds for the kiln staff.

Hubert Baker, the council roadman, was contacted to confirm that he could have time off from the council once more to do the hop drying. Adam Jones, who did a lot of contract sheepshearing, had to be contacted in case bending over sheep had crippled him, and he would no longer be able to do the bushelling. It never did and he always could. An advertisement for hop pickers and sometimes for a booker had to be placed in the Bromyard paper. Bank staff on holiday were viewed warily because a bank manager had once stood in for his son for a day and the arithmetical mistakes he had made had caused a lot of trouble.

The Bromyard News & Record
17 August 1933

the slightest suspicion of wilt is observed (evidenced by total dying of the plant), the Ministry of Agriculture will be immediately informed. When looking for wilt I do not consider any other pest or disease whatsoever: it is so important to spot any infection immediately that there must be no distraction. Looking for normal pests is an entirely different operation.

August

On most varieties burr will develop into full hop during this month and picking could possibly start during the last week.

In order to examine the crop thoroughly it is necessary to use a ladder as plants that are otherwise clean can have pests and diseases hidden in the top growth which cannot possibly be seen from the ground, and ignorance of their presence, particularly in the hops picked last, can lead to the development of a completely unsaleable mess.

Last minute servicing of the hop-picking machine, hop-drying burners, kiln equipment and bine hauling equipment will be carried out. Lastly the kilns will be swept out—an Augean task if they have been used for corn drying, because of the vast quantities of dust that will have been deposited throughout.

Hopyard at Upper Lyde in mid-summer with the house and new kilns on the skyline.

September

Fuggle hops of the best value were usually picked on about September 25th and this was borne in mind when deciding when to start. Fuggles were the only hops grown at Little Froome. Other factors had to be considered of course, such as ripeness of the hops and how long the picking was likely to last. A few days before the appointed one, the cribs were placed on the headland of the yard where the start was to be made, and all was ready.

Whether natural early risers or not, the pickers arrived early on the first day to ensure they could have cribs to their liking. Pole pullers, so called because their job originally consisted of pulling down the poles for the hops to be picked in the days before wirework, would carry the cribs into the 'houses' to be picked. They had the impossible task of working out a rational system of moving cribs forward into the yard so that no picker could complain of having small hops to pick all the time. No system was good enough to quell all complaints, particularly from the less industrious who were not to be moved until they had tidied the space round their cribs and picked all the loose hops off the ground. Yard staff quickly developed skins of

September

Although the area of hops in England has decreased, the size of the average hop unit has increased and we are no exception. In spite of mechanisation, this still means that we have to begin picking earlier and, indeed, pick hops that thirty years ago the trade would have considered too green. Fortunately trade preferences have altered regarding colour, although we may be sacrificing a certain amount of yield and alpha-acid if we start too early. Consistently early picking causes serious depletion in rootstock food reserves so we have to 'ring the changes' each year with the choice of which yard to pick first.

Nowadays, the optimum time to pick hops at Upper Lyde is usually the first three weeks in September: it is very difficult, although by no means impossible, to keep hops to a sufficiently high standard to be worth picking afterwards. Two shifts per day are worked, and two twenty foot square kilns, each of three tiers gives us ample capacity to deal with the drying and bagging. Apart from the drier and two or three men in the kiln, approximately twenty people are employed on each shift, about half of them students.

Polepuller cutting 'flags'.

Bushelling at Little Froome. Sid Taylor, Harry Paske, Janet Cook, Walter Lloyd, Adam Jones and Michael Paske.

Using a "crow's nest" to reach the bines.

September (cont)

pachydermal impermeability which were only rarely punctured sufficiently to elicit retaliation.

Three times a day Adam Jones, the busheller, would shout, "Clear 'em up" and clamber round the hopyard, measuring the hops with the cane basket, out of the cribs and into the greensacks. The booker entered the amount picked onto the picker's card and also into the housebook kept for a check, and the pole pullers held open, tied, and loaded the full greensacks onto the tractor-drawn trailer to be taken to the kilns. Here the two kilnmen carried

September (cont)

Four or five work in the hopyard. The hop bines are cut with a hook three or four feet above ground level by a man (or woman) in front of the tractor and trailer. The ends are grabbed by two people on the front of the trailer as it moves through, and the bines are then severed from the top wires by a man with a hook standing on a "crow's nest" frame temporarily fixed on the back. He has to be pretty lively to cut bines from both sides as the trailer moves forward, without being decapitated by the cross wires. Although such an accident is a possibility it has never happened yet. In fact a careless operator would be more likely to carry

September (cont)

and tipped them onto the horse-hair covered drying floor for Hubert Baker to fluff up and level off with a fork. Kiln loading finished, roll sulphur was weighed and ignited with a red hot horseshoe in the sulphur pans below the hops. (The amount of sulphur would be later adjusted on the advice of the hop factor when he examined a dried sample). The fans were started, the automatic stokers put into operation, and ten to twelve hours later the three kilnmen would remove the dried hops on the carrier hairs and tip them in a heap in the cooling room.

Once the building was warm, Little Froome had sufficient room to store the hops for two days before putting them into the pockets. This enabled the residual moisture to redistribute itself in the hop cones, so that they changed from the brittle, dry hop immediately after drying, to acquire a soft, silky feel that enabled them to be scuppered across the floor into the hole where the pocket was suspended, without suffering any damage from shattering. One man pushed the hops up to the bagger, one turned the bagger handle which was geared well down so that the press exerted a consolidating pressure on the hops, and Hubert Baker kept an eye on the pocket from down below and sewed up and weighed it on completion. The pockets, which were marked with consecutive numbers, were all kept on the premises until after harvest, but all those with a number ending in a 5 were put on one side for priority delivery to the warehouse. This was because the Hop Marketing Board needed them to obtain 'type' samples to assist in valuation of the crop and would not pay out the first instalment of payment until all '5s' had been delivered.

Hops were picked on five days a week if the weather was good: very few pickers would brave very wet weather which was just as well because of the mess that would be caused by the hopyard traffic. If harvest was behindhand picking was done on Sundays when more than usual would be picked because of extra people from Bromyard who would be available. In some late seasons Little Froome pickers would be augmented when Tos Adams at Avenbury Court finished, or vice versa if Little Froome finished first.

September (cont)

out such an operation with his own hook. It is certainly always necessary to warn the hopyard gang of the danger of the cutting hooks—if this warning is ever neglected on the first day of hop picking someone invariably has to be taken to the casualty department for stitching up during the opening hours of the season.

Three tractor drivers are employed driving hops to the picking machine. Here the bines are pushed into clamps which carry them through three banks of rotating plucker fingers which strip away the cones. The resulting mixture of hop and leaf is separated by a strong air current which sucks out the leaves; the hops are further improved by passing over cascades of inclined belts which allow them to roll down and waste materials to be carried over the top. Two or three of the older ladies of the staff, who are much more efficient than anyone else at the job, remove the remaining rubbish before the hops are elevated to the top floor of the kiln and deposited in bins ready for drying.

The hop drier and kiln men take over now. The loaded bins are pushed into the drying chamber. These are built with perforated platten bottoms which open to release the hops to a central drying floor. This is also built with perforated plattens. These open to release the hops into nylon mesh bins immediately above the plenum chamber into which the centrifugal fans of the burners force the hot air. When fully in operation three tiers of hops are thus being dried with the same hot air simultaneously. Each batch has about seven to nine hours drying time.

When the hops are dry, two men tip them out of the nylon bins into a heap for moisture redistribution to take place. The bagger is an old hand machine, now electrically powered by an apparatus built by the late Harold Edwards of Collington, and presses hops into the still conventional 'pockets'. As we have insufficient storage the pockets are sent into Ledbury warehouse as soon as a load is ready. Nowadays we use our own transport in order to lessen the chances of picking up wilt from lorries that have been hauling from infected farms. So far we have been able to choose a route that avoids driving by infected farms but that will soon be impossible because of the way the disease is spreading.

Feeding the hop-picking machine.

Removing leaf and strig from the hops.

Walter Dew, a hop drier from an old Bromyard family, is levelling off hops being tipped on to the drying floor of the kiln by his son. Note the carrying hairs hooked on to the walls, which were unhooked to remove the dried hops.

Dried hops being scuppered into the pocket for compression by the electrically-driven plunger. The motor and controls in the box were made by Harold Edwards of Collington in the '50s. Nowadays the open wheel would have to be guarded.

Pockets have had to be numbered consecutively since the last century. EEC regulations decree additional markings which are applied with a stencil.

Each pocket of hops is weighed. A constant weight is an indication of good drying management.

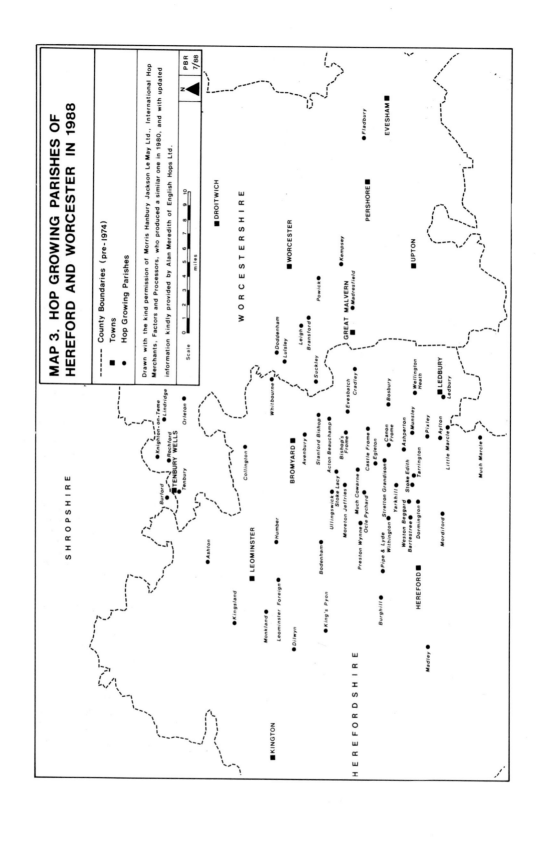

MAP 3. HOP GROWING PARISHES OF HEREFORD AND WORCESTER IN 1988

----- County Boundaries (pre-1974)

■ Towns

● Hop Growing Parishes

Drawn with the kind permission of Morris Hanbury Jackson Le May Ltd., International Hop Merchants, Factors and Processors, who produced a similar one in 1980, and with updated information kindly provided by Alan Meredith of English Hops Ltd.

Scale
0 1 2 3 4 5 6 7 8 9 10
miles

N

PBR
7/88

SHROPSHIRE

HEREFORDSHIRE

WORCESTERSHIRE

■ KINGTON

■ DROITWICH

● Kingsland
● Monkland
● Leominster Foreign
■ LEOMINSTER
● Humber
● Ashton
● Dilwyn

● Burford
■ TENBURY WELLS
● Tenbury
● Rochford
● Knighton-on-Teme
● Lindridge
● Orleton

● Collington

● Whitbourne
● Doddenham
● Lulsley
● Leigh
● Bransford
● Powick
● Suckley
● Kempsey
■ WORCESTER

● Madley
● King's Pyon
● Bodenham

■ BROMYARD
● Avenbury
● Stanford Bishop
● Acton Beauchamp
● Ullingswick
● Stoke Lacy
● Moreton Jeffries
● Much Cowarne
● Bishop's Frame
● Castle Frome
● Egleton
● Canon Frome
● Evesbatch
● Cradley

■ GREAT MALVERN
● Madresfield
● Fladbury
■ PERSHORE

● Burghill
● Pipe & Lyde
● Preston Wynne
● Ocle Pychard
● Stretton Grandison
● Weston Beggard
● Withington
● Yarkhill
■ HEREFORD
● Bartestree
● Dormington
● Stoke Edith
● Tarrington
● Asperton
● Munsley
● Pixley
● Bosbury
● Wellington Heath
■ LEDBURY
● Ledbury
■ UPTON

■ EVESHAM

● Mordiford
● Aylton
● Little Marcle
● Much Marcle

CHAPTER 10

Modern Developments in Hop Growing

'Considerable quantities of hops are grown in Herefordshire; especially about Bromyard; - in that part of the county bordering on what may be called the Hop District of Worcestershire.'

William Marshall, 1745-1818.

Few industries have changed more than hop growing in the last seventy years. The fundamental part, the hop has changed, cultivation, pest disease, and weed control, picking, drying and marketing have altered, and the growers and their labour have had to develop entirely different skills.*

Scientific research has played a great part. This used to take place only at Wye College and East Malling Research Station, both starting in Kent in the latter half of the last century, but in 1949 the Ministry of Agriculture bought the 176 hectare Rosemaund Farm only eight miles south-west of Bromyard and developed it into an experimental husbandry farm. It is still the only Ministry of Agriculture establishment with hops. The 16 hectares of hops already there were progressively grubbed and new hops planted on fresh ground. In January 1959 the first *Report on the Experimental Work on Hops* by E. L. Jones, the farm director, and N. Moss, the hops manager, appeared. This imparted information discovered about subjects such as cultivations, manuring, dressing and training, and observations on 'New Varieties', all of which were of immediate concern to growers, particularly those farming under similar conditions in the Bromyard area.

The big chemical firms also played a part: in the 1930s I.C.I. did experiments at Dormington Court, outside Hereford, showing that hops could be grown satisfactorily with artificial fertilizers in the total absence of organic manures, and since the war the big companies have continuously developed chemicals for pest, disease, and weed control, many of which have been tested at Rosemaund prior to and concurrently with farm use. Since the 1950s G. P. Chater, who took over as director after E. L. Jones, and F. Dickens, who succeeded N. Moss as hops manager, together with the specialist hop advisers from the government advisory services at Litley Court, must have visited all the hop farms in the Bromyard area, giving profitable advice based on Rosemaund trials, to growers in difficulty. It is well known that it is easier to get into difficulties with hops than with any other crop on this planet and a plot of hops is certainly no bed of roses.

Hop Varieties

Pressures of economic and plant health have imposed the adoption of new varieties, and Ray Neve, O.B.E., who retired in 1984 from managing the breeding programme of Wye College, was so successful that brewers found difficulty in testing his 'offspring' quickly enough to develop the processes required to use them.

---

* This and the following chapters have been contributed by Harry Paske.

The object of breeding is to combine genes responsible for alpha acid (which determines the bitterness and preservative value), aroma, high yield, specific disease and pest resistance, vigour (subject to suitability for modern machine picking), and tolerance to difficult conditions and any agricultural malpractice the grower can manage.

It is amazing that in spite of the tremendous popularity of new varieties with growers and brewers, the aroma hops, Golding and Fuggle, introduced in the late 18th and 19th centuries respectively, still occupy 20% of the total area. They have been reselected several times, but are all descended from the original stock. Between 1950-70 Fuggles decreased to 40% because of wilt. Fuggles, a coarser hop than Goldings, are able to tolerate the cold, sticky Bromyard soils rather better, but are less valuable. Some yards of these varieties, for instance at Burlton Court when farmed by the late Phil Hodell and at Nunnington when farmed by Mr Garlick, are known to have been grown continously for a century, and in the course of gapping up dead stocks, some yards have even gradually changed over from one variety to another. I suspect that the present laws relating to description of goods would often have been contravened. The story is quite true about the Bromyard farmer who, while walking his growing crop was asked by his hop factor which yard the Goldings were in, replied 'Well, I haven't really made up my mind yet for this year.'

Variety confusion has also occurred on an international scale. Yugoslavia used to obtain Fuggle and Golding plants from England after the First World War, selling the resulting crops to British hop merchants. When the fungus disease, downy mildew, appeared in the 1920s, it was fatal to the Goldings in that climate and more Golding roots were imported only to suffer the same fate. The Fuggles, however, were able to effectively withstand the disease and the hops have since been imported into Britain as 'Styrian Goldings'.

The original source of new varieties was North America, the first successful one a seedling discovered in Manitoba in 1916 and named Bullion. It had the advantages of twice the yield of contemporary cultivated hops and a high although variable alpha acid content (bittering property). Extreme vigour and coarse bine made it difficult to pick by hand and when eventually picked mechanically it would often cause damage if the machinery was badly operated. This was not the main disadvantage: it had an exceptionally strong aroma, similar to blackcurrant, which degraded on becoming stale to the characteristic stink known, with comparative euphemism, as 'tom-cat'. Fortunately brewers overcame this. Guinness, who are now the main users of Bullion, rid their product of this feline attribute by simply boiling it away.

Northern Brewer, a hop of more moderate growth, was developed by crossbreeding in 1934 and has the benefit of comparatively high alpha acid (the latest selection of the stock has even higher values because it is bred virus-free) and an aroma similar to that of Goldings. Unfortunately it is rather susceptible to powdery mildew and without modern fungicides would probably never have survived in the Bromyard area. Nevertheless it was a very successful hop. Apart from being popular here it was grown in Belgium, at one time comprising over 65% of that country's total hop area. From there the German hop growers took it up, under the impression that it was a Belgian hop. This misapprehension disturbed the British breeders so much that they added the prefix 'Wye' to the names of varieties produced during the '70s and 'Wye Northdown' and 'Wye Challenger' appeared. These were good yielding hops with, for that time, high alpha acid content and had the additional advantage of resistance to fungus diseases. Unfortunately this resistance broke down after a few years to a more active mutant of powdery mildew so that even these varieties now require protective treatment.

One of the latest hops being grown in the region is Zenith, but lack of demand for hops generally has considerably delayed its popularity. It is a very high alpha hop which some find difficult to grow because of an alleged inability to climb the hop string. Tony Sanderson from Newnham Bridge, however, says he has no trouble with them, perhaps because he has good windbreaks. A windy June makes it difficult for any hop to climb. At one time it was thought that Zenith would be very good for lager, which now accounts for 50% of the beer drunk in this country, but unfortunately this hop has not been as popular with brewers generally, as had been hoped.

Avant-garde growers like Victor Stock of Tarrington are growing the very high alpha variety 'Omega' under licence from Wye College but this has had very few brewing trials yet so they are sticking their necks out. This could be so that they can cut their own throats because, of course, the more high alpha hops are produced the less the brewer needs to make the same quantity of beer. Hops are increasingly being sold purely according to the weight of alpha acid: this means that a hop with a feasible alpha of 10% would earn double the money per acre of one of 5%, which is a good alpha for the old fashioned varieties or even possibly for a high alpha variety under some kind of stress. Fortunately for the grower of Fuggles and Goldings the remuneration is not yet entirely on so simplistic a basis, for the flavour-hops have properties absent in new varieties.

New varieties at present only being grown on the outskirts of the region are the wilt tolerants. These can withstand the mycelium of the fatal (to other hop varieties) fungus disease, verticillium wilt. This spreads from the root-hairs through the vascular tissues and produces toxins which kill the complete plant including the stock. This highly infectious disease has driven many people out of hop growing in Kent, where it appeared in 1924. Occasional outbreaks have occurred in Herefordshire since the war but were all extinguished until the present outbreak started in the Lower Frome Valley in 1975. There are now over twenty-eight confirmed outbreaks and the nearest to Bromyard is five miles away down the Frome Valley. This disease is the AIDS of the hop world and there is no known cure. Wilt is notifiable and orders are made to grub infected plants and fifty-four plants surrounding each one, fence off the area, and grass it down. Very strict hygienic precautions must be taken subsequently. Some farmers consider they have destroyed the disease by going to the trouble and expense of grubbing a complete hopyard for the sake of only one or two infected plants, but others have not been so successful: the disease has cropped up in nearby hopyards afterwards. Wilt tolerant hops may only be grown under licence from the Ministry of Agriculture because of the danger of concealed infection if the plants should happen to become symptomless carriers. Wye Target, a very high alpha hop, is the one at present being grown and only four farms in the area have licence to do so.*

* Since this article was written the regulations regarding planting of wilt tolerant varieties have been altered and subject to certain conditions any grower can now plant them.

At present Wye College is having a certain amount of success in attempting to breed a dwarf variety of hop to alleviate the problems of high wirework and make harvesting a great deal easier, enabling mobile picking machines to operate much more efficiently. The majority of hops nowadays have to be transported to stationary picking machines. At Rosemaund normal varieties have been grown to a height of only six feet with disappointing yields so far, although valuable technical information has been obtained.

Cultivations

The old system of earthing up the hops in June, in order to smother the weeds and prevent further basal growth, required the removal of the soil in early spring the next year so that the ground pegs for the string could be set right, and the old bine cut back to the crown of the plant to prevent stocks becoming too big and having shoots grow up all over the hopyard. At Little Froome the practice was to plough two furrows width away from the hops with a standard Fordson tractor and Ransomes hop plough, finishing off the job by ploughing as close as possible to the roots with an old Kell swing plough which was designed for horses but used behind a tractor with a drawbar adaptation. A walking man still controlled the plough from behind and would soon become the most unpopular person on the farm if he left too much soil to be stocked away by the following gang. Stocking away the soil to clear the hops which one then cut back to the crown with a crank-ed hook, known as 'throwing down and cutting', was one of the hardest jobs I have ever done. To add insult to injury I used to work alongside Jim Walton, an eighty-year-old countryman who was by then half blind. 'Alongside' is the wrong word; he did the job literally twice as fast as I could and I never saw him sweat or heard him grunt. But he did spit on his hands.

Before the modern *No Cultivation* system the first spring cultivation was ploughing the soil away from the hops. This was a hydraulic David Brown plough adapted by the Bruff Company.

If conditions were not good enough for the 3-furrow plough to do a good job, a swing plough - here a Kell - was controlled by the ploughman to leave as narrow a furrow as possible.

An alternative tool for removing the ridge was the kerf, or stocker, here framed by the cranked cutting hook stuck into the pole in readiness for the next operation.

It was no wonder that attempts were made to alleviate this hard labour! The Bruff Company of Suckley and Ted Wargent of Canon Frome eventually developed machines which were operated from the power-take-off points of tractors and flailed the soil from the hop rows with rotating arms. These machines had to straddle the hop rows in order to work and so were made with ingenious mechanisms to move them out of the way when they came to a pole.

The system still suffered from the disadvantage of having tractors on the ground at a time of year when soil was often wet enough to be compacted. Compaction restricts root growth and is nowadays ameliorated by implements which are drawn through the ground to shatter the compressed layers when conditions are dry enough in autumn. It is preferable but almost impossible not to cause the compaction in the first place and Rosemaund E.H.F. experimented with the idea of not ploughing hops at all, but grassing them down and keeping the grass short, so that compaction damage in the wetter months could be kept to a minimum. This system was hardly ever used outside the experimental farm because grass robbed the hops of nitrogen and had to be continuously mown during the summer with gang mowers.

This Bruff 'throwing down' machine used rotating tines to throw the soil from the hops, leaving very little to be removed by hand tools.

The final operation, where the shoots were cut back to the crown of the plant. The handle of the cutting hook was cranked so that the worker's hand kept clear of the ground.

Since then the practice of 'non-cultivation' has been developed in which the ground is kept clear of weeds by spraying with simazine and paraquat. Simazine is a pre-emergence weed killer which kills seedlings at germination and paraquat kills any green growth that it touches. With the recently developed systemic herbicides which can kill creeping grasses without harming hops there is now no need to cultivate hops with implements at all, except to incorporate farmyard manure, and many farmers such as Charles Pudge of the Frogend, Castle Frome, do manage their yards in this way.

Environmentalists need not worry about the use of herbicides. Cowslips now grow and flower among my hops where under the traditional system they were absent.

It is still advisable to cut back the old remaining bine to ground level each year because of the risk of it harbouring pests and disease. The backbending necessary with the use of a cranked cutting hook for this job is avoided by some growers by using a small, motorised rotary cutter hung from a harness on the operator.

Manuring

Most growers use an organic fertilizer such as farmyard manure or slurry as a basal fertilizer and it is generally considered to be advantageous to the humus content and thus the structure of the soil. This has not actually been proven under the conditions of modern non-cultivation methods and it may no longer be necessary. Some of the fertilizer firms have developed pelleted semi-organic fertilizer which they claim to be better than pure, so called, artificial manures because of the more gradual release of some of the nutrients. I am not convinced that this slight advantage justifies the extra expense of these fertilizers. In fact I have not used any kind of organic fertilizer on hops for several years. Time available for application was in the winter months and damage done to wet soil, particularly on the Bromyard series*, by tractors and muck-spreaders was much more than any benefit accruing from using fertilizer in organic form. Neither do I believe that dung from a pedigree Hereford bull worth £30,000 is any more use than that from a store bullock worth £300. However if the muck is available, cheap, and conditions are right, FYM is quite a useful crop nutrient although the chemical contents can only be estimated.

ADAS (Agricultural Development and Advisory Service) or fertilizer agents will analyse the soil and inform the farmer of its status of phosphate, potassium and magnesium on an index of 0-6 and lime according to pH value. Hopyard soil samples are taken at two depths below the surface, $0''-6''$ and $6''-12''$. These give an indication of how quickly the nutrients move down through the soil and requirements for future years. Starting a new hopyard on a fresh site it would not be impossible to have indices of 0. In this case applications of perhaps 280 lbs per acre of phosphate as P_2O_5 and 400 lbs per acre of potash as K_2O may be necessary. According to conditions, the phosphate index with this type of application could very well build up to 3 after a few years when only 200 lbs per year would need to

*soils are scientifically classified into 'series', each of which is given the name of a locality.

be applied. Potash would not build up so fast but it would certainly increase in Bromyard soils so that much less would be needed with regular application. A rare possibility that may occur in a very dry season is magnesium deficiency, promoted by excess potassium and giving the leaves a very pretty bright yellow edge. Epsom salts is the answer to this.

Hops have always been considered reasonably tolerant to acidity down to pH 6.0, but recently, using BDH indicator, much lower pH has been found in patches of hops in a yard, subsequently the hops failing completely because of particularly localised lime shortage. A soil sample properly taken gives only an average of the yard's condition, so nowadays a pH of 6.0 most likely requires immediate treatment, because some areas would be less.

There is no point in analysing soil for nitrogen as its availability varies so much throughout the year and nitrates are so easily leached away in winter. Work done at Wye College in the '30s and '40s indicated an optimum response at 270 lbs of nitrogen per acre and at one time I used to follow that practice. Unfortunately twenty years ago it was difficult to drive fertilizer spreaders so accurately as today and great dollops of nitrogen fertilizer used to be dropped in the end ten yards of the rows as the tractor drove slower on entering and leaving. Consequently growth became so 'housey' that nests of the pigeons that took advantage of the leaves were sometimes invisible until the bines were pulled at hop picking. Nowadays, with research at Rosemaund having been taken into consideration, nitrogen recommendations have been decreased, and if wilt is a danger, no more than 170 lbs per acre should be used. Some growers manage with even less but their soils probably have a higher humus content.

Pests, Diseases and Problems

Growers in the Bromyard area were introduced to modern pest and disease control and equipment by Pest Control Ltd., the contractors who took over the army searchlight post just out of town on the Hereford road after the war. In the past aphids have probably been responsible for more damage to growing hops than any other agent, and before reasonable control measures were available in the late 19th century they often had a devastating effect. Ladybirds and their larvae were known to destroy this pest and swallows, also, had often been observed destroying quantities of the winged form as they left the hopyards for their winter quarters on plum, damson and blackthorn. Although this would have been a satisfying sight to a grower the fact that this activity was evident at all meant that sufficient fly had been breeding to have already done considerable damage to the crop. Unfortunately, according to the Board of Agriculture's leaflet no. 55, *The Swallow,* published in 1904, swallows had become so reduced in numbers that their influence in keeping down hop flies was very much less effective than formerly. But, to quote the leaflet: 'It is said by some observers that the regular recurrence of hop aphis attack known as "blight" year after year and their alarmingly increasing intensity are due to the absence of swallows. This increase is, however, more probably due to the plan of planting prunes (sic) in the alley.'

During and up to the end of the Second World War aphids had been mainly controlled by nicotine powder blown by a dusting machine. The operation needed doing in still air so that the dust would hang in the hops and because the job was so urgent was often done overnight, the men carrying on with haymaking in the daytime. Similarly very fine sulphur dust would be applied for mould, and Bordeaux powder as a preventative for downy mildew.

It was a relief to be able to delegate the job to a contractor, particularly as the new chemical sprays developed from war gases were so effective. One could walk down the hop row behind the sprayer, being covered by the aphids as sudden death made them relinquish their grip on the leaves. By natural selection aphids gradually acquired resistance and even immunity to the original aphicides, new ones having to be continually developed. Pest control has now became a race against the pest's ability to adapt against chemicals.

An early Drake and Fletcher hop-powdering machine driven by Ned Watkins. Note the hurricane lamp for night work.

Since the war we have been fortunate to have had two products which when applied to the roots and absorbed into the sap killed any aphid that sucked. The first one, used originally in the early 1950s was named Terra Sytam by the makers—Terra because it was applied to the soil at the base of the bines, and Sytam, an acronym for Save Your Time and Mine, which it certainly did in the early days because no subsequent aphid treatment would be required. It was unfortunately necessary to wear a gas mask when handling the concentrated material because a good sniff when pouring it into the spray tank could be fatal. There were several occasions when people had alarming experiences from slight splashes onto the face. This chemical became gradually outdated and its replacement, cytrolane, is even more efficient and to date there has been no sign of any resistance to it. Problems only occur in very dry years when sap movement is sluggish.

Red spider is a mite which can probably destroy hops quicker than anything else. Fortunately it only occurs in very hot weather, but it is so small that most people cannot see it with the naked eye. If infection is suspected because of the peculiar brown tinge of the leaves, a useful test is to spread fine dust onto the underside of the leaf. This makes apparent the fine web spun by the creature. Immediate treatment with a modern chemical is essential but effective, so long as it is not a spray to which the mite is becoming immune.

Fungus diseases also acquire resistance, and a narrow escape against this eventuality has just occurred with the use of Ridomil, a completely effective systemic chemical against downy mildew. This had previously been just as effective against potato blight but the disease had developed resistance after only two years of commercial use. The makers now only sell Ridomil as a mix with copper, the active ingredient of the old Bordeaux mixture, and this new two-pronged attack, the Ridomil acting systemically in the sap of the plant and the copper preventing external infection, has remained successful on hops to date. The Agricultural Development and Advisory Service runs a downy mildew warning system which notifies growers of specific downy mildew danger periods. Unfortunately some years just seem to be a continuous danger period so we have to use a downy mildew prophylactic every time we spray, anyway.

The practice of stripping the lower three or four foot of bine of leaves is a protection from powdery mildew because it prevents spores leaf-hopping from the ground to the upper parts of the plant. This used to be done by hand but is now carried out with defoliant sprays. As the sprayer cannot be selective, weak hops are protected by transparent polythene sleeves during the whole season.

Most farmers spray their own hops now. Several factors have caused this: haymaking is not such hard work as it was, expert advice is available from Ministry of Agriculture and commercial advisers, hops need treatment more often, and there is the very great danger of rampant verticillium wilt infection from tractors and machines travelling from farm to farm.

In order to prevent unnecessary treatment and to make necessary treatment more timely and effective, pest and disease warning systems have been developed. Rosemaund E.H.F. has a weather station which collects data relevant to the spread of disease and pests—humidity, temperature, rainfall, etc, as well as a spore trap with which diseases moving through the atmosphere can be identified. There are several other such sites on hop farms in the area and the information can be used to save the grower a lot of money. The most astoundingly accurate service is the forecast of the fly-in of the aphid from the damson and blackthorn trees in the first half of June. During the last few years, the forecasts, made a month previously, have been accurate to within twenty-four hours. Unfortunately in 1986 the forecast was ten days early.

In certain seasons hops have a tendency to produce leaves from between the petals of the cone itself, and the varieties which are particularly prone to this aberration, Northern Brewer and Northdown, can be downgraded in valuation if affected hops are present. It has been discovered that production of these 'cock' hops can be prevented by spraying a natural plant hormone, gibberellic acid, specifically when the plant is producing its fifteenth node, usually at a height of about 5'6" during the third week in May. It may be necessary to spray twice with a few days interval in order to catch the maximum number of bines at the right stage. This treatment delays the production of the 'burr' by about a week, consequently producing more. The resultant hops tend to be smaller but the actual weight produced is heavier more often than not.

Virus disease is perhaps the most complex problem of all. Sufficient information has been obtained during the last twenty years to facilitate effective control, but for some time scientists could only infer the existence of some of the viruses. Nettlehead, which mainly attacks Fuggles, is visually the most obvious disease and is probably caused by a combination of three different viruses. The effect is a general weak growth from early in the season later causing the growing tips, unable to climb, to fall back from the string. The leaves develop a similarity to nettle leaves only producing one tip instead of three lobes. In some seasons growth will improve in good growing weather but the plant declines over the years, although rarely dying out completely. In the past this fact has encouraged growers to continue producing hops from infected yards which were becoming increasingly worse and losing a lot of money.

Mosaic, a disease of which Fuggle is only a symptomless carrier but which affects Goldings, is a completely different matter. This may kill the plant in one or two years and in badly infected areas it may be difficult to keep a hopyard in existence for ten years, especially if the Goldings are grown close to Fuggles or other carrier varieties.

Virus disease also considerably decreases the alpha acid content, a serious economic factor with the new varieties. In the 1960s East Malling Research Station in Kent discovered that one of the main culprits, the arabis mosaic virus, was transmitted through the soil in the body of an eelworm, the 'dagger' nematode, a threadlike creature about a millimetre long. Rosemaund E.H.F. later collaborated in trials, fumigating soil in an infected hopyard with a cultivating tool that injected a sterilant into the ground and counting the eelworms present before and after. These trials were combined and compared with varying periods of fallowing the hop ground. Without fumigation a fallow period of two years was necessary to destroy the nematodes but a fallow period of only one year was necessary if the soil was sterilised, a considerable economic saving. Soil sterilisation is a very specialised job and until 1986 there was only one machine in the West Midlands capable of doing it.

The buds on hop setts are a delicacy greatly appreciated by slugs and if there are too many to share in the feast they can cause substantial losses in a young crop. Proponents of organic agricultural methods will probably say that slug damage is inevitable, as slugs are also found on rotting materials, and if they are deprived will presumably have to make the most of what remains available. But the modern methiocarb pellets are remarkably effective slug desiccants. Five pounds per acre are all that are necessary even in a corn crop. Slugs rarely recover from contact even in wet weather, and the pellets remain effective in the open for much longer than metaldehyde mixes used to. Even environmentalists need have no worries: the chemical engineers who developed the poison deliberately made it blue, a colour to which birds are apparently not attracted.

Peter Davies of Claston, in the Lower Frome Valley, who had a serious nettlehead problem in most of his hopyards, was also collaborating with Mike Thresh and his team of scientists from East Malling and by 1970 was confident enough of the trial results to plan a grubbing, fumigating and fallowing system in order to change over to new varieties. By 1976 he had been so successful that only ten infected plants could be found in his seventy acres of hops.

Propagation, Planting and Training

Because it is essential to plant only virus free stock after the expense of fumigation and fallowing, the traditional system for planting has been superseded. Many farms used to collect the best cuttings resulting from throwing down in March, plant them in a nursery bed over the summer to develop roots, and lift them in the autumn ready to plant straight into the yard as well-developed setts, the amount of development depending on the weather during the growing period. If the hops from which the cuttings were taken were infected so would the plants from the setts be. Every November the Ledbury auctioneers, C. T. and G. H. Smith used to auction hop roots in the market, until the local verticillium wilt outbreaks made it too dangerous from a plant health point of view. Nowadays, roots are bought from specialist suppliers of stock certified free from virus by Ministry of Agriculture inspectors. These suppliers are in areas where hops are not grown commercially for picking: Norfolk, Suffolk, and Powys.

In order to multiply hops quickly, if for instance a sudden demand occurs for a new variety, cuttings can be taken from the lateral branches and grown on in pots in a heated mist house. When developed enough these can be planted straight into the yard after a suitable hardening off period, even in the middle of summer. Very little disturbance need upset the roots if they are grown in Jiffy pots which dissolve in the soil so do not need to be removed.

Runners produced by established hops can become a nuisance, producing new plants at every node and in some cases even forming a 'hedge' down the row if the cutting back of the previous year's dead bine has not been tidily executed. The

Training hops round the string was an [ard]uous kneeling-down job, and the same [syst]em is still fairly general; but the ['ass]isted self training' method practised [by]some growers can be carried out from [a]standing position.

difficulty occurs at hop tying when selection of the bines for the string can become a problem because the best ones cannot be identified in the conglomeration of shoots.

Rosemaund E.H.F. has developed a way of preventing this circumstance by planting setts in polypropylene tubes which are produced by local plastic extrusion firms. Sufficient roots have to protrude below the tubes to be in contact with the soil, but as long as the buds are sheathed they have to shoot upwards, and are thus prevented from producing runners along the surface.

This system simplifies hop tying, and also makes the 'assisted self training' method of growing more effective. Unwanted bines are not ripped out by hand as in normal tying: workers merely walk through and ensure that each string is furnished with at least three bines (or whatever quantity is required). The surplus basal growth is removed by spraying a defoliant directed downwards. For an, as yet, unexplained reason this system produces lower yields than the traditional way, so very few growers practice it in this area. I use the method myself and will not alter now because so much more labour would be needed posing a much greater chance of contracting verticillium wilt.

Winding hop string in Pettifer's workroom at 7 High Street, Bromyard, as it was until the 1960s.

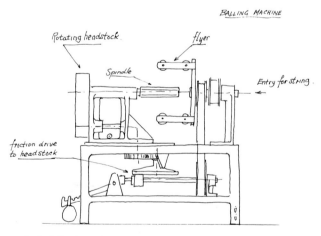

BALLING MACHINE

Rotating headstock.

flyer

Spindle

Entry for string.

friction drive
to headstock

The ready spun and plied (2 ply) coir came from India in compressed bales suitably wrapped and strengthened with canes, which were hoisted from the carts in Little Hereford Street to the workroom on the top floor. Once unwrapped the ready-made hanks of string were unravelled from the bale and placed on the 'dolly', a revolving conical cone standing about 4 feet high at the side of the balling machine. The end of the string was fed through the hollow shaft, round the pulleys on the 'flyer' and tied on to the spindle of the headstock. When the spindle and flyer were rotating the string was wound into a ball, or rather a cheese shape, by moving the angle of the spindle with a handle attached to the moveable headstock. Pettifer marketed the hop string under the trade name 'Samson'.

About 800 United Kingdom farmers grew hops in the '50s, but now the number is down to less than 320, so implement makers for the industry have not benefited from the advantages of scale in the way that other manufacturers have. In the early days of the tractor, however, general farm cultivating implements, having been designed for horses, were small enough to travel hop rows anyway and only slight alterations to the hitching arrangements were necessary. Ransomes of Ipswich used to make special hop ploughs and heavy disc cultivators, and Craven of Evesham were among the first makers of dusting and spraying equipment in the days of the horse. The main local suppliers of specific hop equipment used to be Wargent Brothers of Stoke Edith (now with Morris, Wargent and Wilde at Whitestone), Ted Wargent of Canon Frome, John Hill of Ledbury and Pettifer of Bromyard. They provided everything the growers needed from complete hop kilns to the steel ground pegs required by each root for the application of the coir yarn for the hops to climb. Cutting 18 inch lengths of 1/4 inch steel rod and forming the hooks was a steady, time consuming job for when business was slack. Each acre required about 1800 pegs.

Pettifer of Bromyard gave up the hop part of the business in the 1960s, and Tony Winwood, a carpet manufacturer from Kidderminster, took over Much Cowarne Rectory in the early 1950s as a warehouse for hop requisites. Hop growers of course have a use for shoddy, the waste from the carpet factory, as a bulky organic fertilizer.

An essential part of a hop sundries supplier's equipment is the balling machine, used for winding into balls the coir yarn made from coconut fibre imported from India. With exotic names like Anjengo or Alapat according to the part of the continent where it originates, this arrives in England, in bales, in the winter months to be balled by local women. Some local growers, such as Neston Capper from Lower Hope, Ullingswick, until he retired in 1984, also have their own balling machines enabling them to find useful work for their own staff during the quieter period of the year. When balled the yarn is taken to the farms to be strung between the ground pegs and the hooks on the top wires forming a trellis for the hops to climb. The tool used for this operation is a 'monkey', a long rod with a tube attached to the side of the one end through which the string from a bag carried by the 'stringer' is threaded and guided from peg to hook. It is a very skilled job to get the string to run quickly and smoothly without cutting through your hand in a few minutes, and a badly wound ball can be frustrating to a novice to the point of dementia if it keeps jamming. Artificial yarns have been developed from polypropylene which are much easier to manipulate with speed. Unfortunately this material degrades in sunlight and when first used on its own a great number of bines fell to the ground later in the season. Brown paper wrapping was used to shade it, but there are still problems. In a windy season hops have difficulty clinging to it and polypropylene does not chop up very easily mechanically if it is necessary to macerate the bine after picking. Length for length polypropylene is cheaper and it is easier to apply than coir, but so far these good points are outweighed by the disadvantages.

Hop wirework systems are still gradually evolving since starting to take over from polework in 1867. Originally wirework was erected to a height of no more

Erecting a new hopyard at Upper Lyde in the severe winter of 1962-63. Norman Watkins and Frank Price fixing the anchor wire to a post.

than 12 feet, but machine picking has encouraged heights of 14'6" to 18' in this country in order to get a more evenly developed bine.

Anyone visiting Kent may have noticed that some of the yards have many more poles supporting the crosswires than is customary in the Bromyard area. This is because in Herefordshire the framework is erected in the correct manner! The difference lies in the use of more strainers, or anchors, which are fixed to old railway sleepers and concrete blocks buried in the ground, and known as 'dead men'. When properly dug in, these can withstand the breaking strain of the wire and this is a far more efficient method than merely doubling the number of inside poles. It is true, however, that Kentish practices are improving!

Constructing hopyards is an extremely skilful occupation and understanding the positioning of poles, wires and anchors in order to withstand the peculiar strains caused by the ridiculous shapes of some hopyard boundaries does take years of experience. Some farmers can do it well, and it is another employment for farm staff during the winter months, but a job I personally can do without. Doing intricate wire splicing at the top of a ladder against an ice covered 18 foot pole in a snowstorm is apt to be uncomfortable even if you don't suffer from vertigo, and if the weather improves on that you can find yourself trudging from pole to pole in a mudbath. It isn't always quite as bad as that of course, but to be on the safe side I always employ a contractor. I can't splice wire anyway.

Erecting the framework at the end of a hop row.

Norman Watkins who erects and maintains my hopyards can do everything that has to be done to, with or for hops. He learnt the job from his father, Ned, who in turn learned it from his father who started in about 1880. None of the family was ever responsible for a yard that collapsed—an almost unbelievable record, but the ultimate calamity if such a thing should happen. It is unfortunately a happening that occurs only too frequently, and of course often when it is a heavy crop approaching harvest in rainy weather. The crop weight is near its maximum and increased considerably by the amount of rain held by the foliage. An equinoctial gale can cause the whole weight to lift free of the supports. If this happens several times and there is just one weak spot, a damaged pole perhaps or anchor wire, the sudden stress as the weight falls back on to the poles and anchors can be enough to collapse the complete framework. Any embarrassment felt by the person responsible for the improper maintenance will be very short-lived because of the effort that will be required to rescue hops from the tangled mass of wires, poles and bines. The wire will have to be cut up and sacrificed in order to load the hops on to trailers, and if the weather remains wet a good many hops will also have to be sacrificed because of mud contamination. A very expensive experience! I will not mention the name of one farmer in the region who once had a yard collapse in winter when there was no crop on it at all!

As wirework height has increased, new methods of assembly have been tried, not all of which have been improvements. Poles used nowadays are usually straight pine impregnated with creosote under pressure. These are unpleasant to handle when freshly treated and a good many growers prefer poles treated with copper and arsenic compounds. These are not so sound, however, and a properly creosoted pole will last a human lifetime, several times the life of the wire attached to it. Oak or sweet chestnut will last a long time without treatment, but the more twisted and knobbly they are the better.

During the war it was difficult to get hopwire and until 1950 permits for it still had to be obtained from the Ministry of Supply. The most common wire in use since then has been a galvanised 7 strand wire, gauge varying according to its particular function. At the end of the war there were hopes of obtaining barrage balloon wire cheaply, but unfortunately it had the wrong tensility and was too difficult to work with so the idea was abandoned. Growers are still alive to all possibilities and when a collapsed hopyard in Kent required speedy re-erection a few years ago surplus wire from the building of the new Humber suspension bridge was available and apparently satisfactory.

The trade has made wireworking much simpler and easier than twenty years ago by producing preformed splices. These only need to be placed by hand round the ends to be joined and will not slip with strains of well over a ton.

New systems have been tried out at Rosemaund E.H.F. in which fewer poles are used and the No. 6 wires to which the string is attached are suspended from a system of catenary wires, instead of being laid over bearing wires as in the old method. We are fortunate to have Rosemaund to iron out snags as this system did collapse one year. Fred Dickens was able to identify and rectify the design fault so that no farmer using the method in future need have the same expensive problem.

Wrapping the No. 6 wire (to which the string will be hooked) to the 'roping' wire at the end of the hopyard.

A wireworker using stilts to put up wire in a new hopyard at Frogend, Castle Frome, about 1980.

CHAPTER 11

Hop-Picking Machines and Drying

'If hops doo looke brownish, then are ye too slowe,
    if longer ye suffer those hops for to growe.
Now sooner ye gather, more profit is found,
    if weather be faire and deaw of a ground.'

Thomas Tusser, 1524?-1580.

Apart from America where machines have catered for much bigger farming operations, Bromyard was the original centre of the development of hop-picking machinery throughout the world. In the 1930s McConnel Hinds of Martley built prototype 'flying finger' hop-picking machines for Norman Edwards of Rosemaund (where the Experimental Husbandry Farm is now), Ernest Griffiths of the Stocks, Suckley, James Bomford of Spring Hill near Pershore, Tom Hawkins at Thinghill Court and Fred Coleman in Kent. After the war, in 1949 Percy Parker at Newton Farm, Stoke Lacy, also had a McConnel Hinds flying finger machine, although by then it was installed by Rubery Owen of Darlaston. This model, however, never subsequently became popular. George Hinds and McConnel later split up and George Hinds continued with hop-picking machines from Barnard's Green, Malvern. He also designed a Rotobank mobile harvester which could be driven from the PTO (power take off) of a tractor or landrover and which he exhibited in Germany. Several attempts have been made by different makers to manufacture mobile picking machines but very few have been sold, perhaps because they tend to be too cumbersome for convenient movement in the restrictive wirework of hopyards, and in wet seasons there would be the fear of being bogged down and causing considerable structural damage to the soil.

The most successful hop-picking machines were developed by the Bruff Manufacturing Company Ltd of Suckley. Mr A. E. Brookes, the first managing director started as a draughtsman for Heenan and Froude of Worcester and also worked as a chemical engineer for a Pershore company. His father-in-law, Mr Bruff, who gave his name to the firm, had been a chemist and developed a fruit tree insecticide which fortuitously turned out to have almost equally effective herbicidal properties, killing fruit trees, and involving him in unfortunate litigation. In 1933 Mr Brookes contracted tuberculosis and had to retire from his work in Pershore. While convalescing he designed a hop-powdering machine and with his father-in-law's help began to manufacture them at Suckley. Mr Bruff died, but Mr Brookes continued designing fruit sprayers, small row crop tractors, hop discs, hop presses and potato harvesters. In 1948 he installed the first prototype Bruff hop-picking machine at Captain Hutton's of Winthill, close to the factory, and the next year four 'A' type machines at Winthill, Les Bowcott's of Monksbury Court, Tom Bowcott's of Felton Court and Charlie Lewis's of Leighton Court. Since then Bruff has exported hop-picking machines to California, Czechoslovakia, Germany, Canada, France, Australia and Poland. In 1962

A McConnel Hinds 'flying-finger' hop-picking machine at Spring Hill near Pershore. The man on the left is loading the bines, still wet with dew, while the woman removes the stripped ones.

This is one of the original A type Bruff hop-picking machines at Monksbury Court in 1949. The gang in front of the tractor is loading bines from the floor on to the hooks of the moving bine track (as in the close-up picture on the left). When the floor is cleared the tractor will move forward and the draw-sheet containing the hop bines will be pulled off its trailer so loading can continue. An empty draw-sheet can be seen thrown up on to the back of the trailer on the right of the photograph. On the platform about 6ft above the floor a woman can be seen removing the picked bines from the moving hooks before they come round to be loaded again.

The machine was moved in two halves on a special axle and the lane from the shed where it was made had to be widened to get it out; it took three days for the journey from Suckley to Yarkhill. Les Bowcott had little idea of how many workers, tractors and trailers he would need and the first year he employed 48 people but by 1960 the number was down to 8. So many visitors came to see the machine working in 1949 that over £400 was collected for the Red Cross.

Waste from a hop-picking machine.

he designed the 'Mini-Bruff' specially for picking on German farms which only grew a few acres each of hops, and 102 were exported. The German firm Scheibenbogen obtained the licence to manufacture those so Bruff did not export any more there. Bruff became part of the Wolseley-Hughes Group in 1968 and by 1978, sales of hop machinery having stagnated through saturation of the market, it was decided to sell the hop side of the operations to CWF Ltd of Ledbury, who have since served the industry well.* In fact they have obtained the licence to manufacture a German machine, the Wolf hop bine loader, which won a silver medal at the 1984 Royal Show, and has done away with the bine loading team of five men in the hopyard. This machine is fitted permanently to the side of a tractor which stays in the hopyard and hitches to the empty trailers returning from the picking machine. As the tractor drives down the row the loader cuts the bine at the bottom, grips it, and releases it at the opportune moment when the tractor has moved forward far enough to pull it from the top wire and deposit it tidily onto the trailer. When fully loaded another tractor takes the trailer to the picking machine. Here operators load the bines onto the bine track, which carries them, inverted, between rotating banks of loop springs which strip them. Any sprays that come off are passed through an automatic spray picker, a moving bed of more loop springs, and the resulting leaves and hops are then passed through a stream of air which sucks out the leaves. There are various ingenious mechanisms for removing bits of strig and everything left passes over inclined, rough surfaced, cascading belts, down which whole hops roll onto the final conveyor for inspection, while any remaining strig and leaf is carried upwards to the waste belt.

The great thing about picking hops by machine is the saving in labour. Unless you have the authority of a field marshal it is impossible to get hundreds of people to do exactly what is required, even if they want to, which is never, and even Montgomery would have been hard put to it in a hopyard. When I bought a machine for 15 acres of hops in 1961 it cut down the picking labour immediately from 100 on the books (which meant over 200 when the families were included) to 14.

*CWF have now given up hop-picking machines and Drake and Fletcher of Kent are the main parts suppliers.

September 1960 was so wet that hand picking in this hopyard was hindered to such an extent that hops were 'let fly'. The farmer bought a picking machine for 1961.

There were several pressures on farmers to accept machines. The expanding economy meant that wages generally were increasing and it was not so necessary for people to earn money for a few weeks in the year. As has already been explained, the time of the school summer holidays was altered and made it difficult for children to be in the yards so the parents could not put in the hours necessary to earn reasonable money. There was always the possibility of a strike by pickers who had a certain advantage because the farmer could never afford to mess about and delay picking.

Wet weather would prevent pickers working. It is not a good thing for the valuation to pick hops in pouring rain, but a day that only started wet could be a complete day wasted with hand pickers. In fact, the quantity of casual labour required made it too unreliable for a modern industry and between 1948 and 1958 the proportion of hops picked by machine rose to 50%, by 1964 the figure was 85% and today all hops are picked by machines.

An advantage of machine picking was that most people who bought a machine were enabled to pick, and therefore grow, more hops than previously, particularly if they were willing to upgrade the machine as improvements to increase efficiency were developed. Hop quota became available as some growers gave up, so the average acreage gradually increased and the industry became more efficient still with the benefits of scale. This enabled the bigger growers particularly, to keep improving mechanisation and the figures kindly given by Peter Walker of Knightwick show this very clearly (see page 145).

Drying

Apart from one ultramodern establishment all hop drying has depended on warm air travelling through a bed of hops from underneath and escaping above it through cowls, louvres or other forms of aperture. The initial temperature must only be allowed to increase slowly otherwise a 'reek' of moisture from the lower layers will condense onto upper layers which are still cool, giving them a dull appearance and lowering the value. The main skill of the drier is in knowing just when to stop drying. The bracts, or petals, will be dry and the strig at the centre of the cone will retain just enough moisture for it to remain tough. After removal from the kiln hops need to be confined in a heap to allow the moisture to redistribute itself into the bracts, making them more supple again and less liable to damage. These facts have had to be borne in mind during the development of all systems of drying from the open fire system to the most modern.

In the Bromyard area modern developments started in the 1920s. With an excess of hops being produced more attention had to be paid to the quality of sample. Some seams of anthracite in use for hop drying had been found to contain arsenic and contamination could occur if open fires were mismanaged. This was really a red herring, caused by arsenical poisoning cases in 1900 being traced to beer, although eventually being found due to sugars used in brewing at the time. However, in times of glut, arsenic content was a valid reason for brewers to refuse hops, so this was a factor in the development of oven type driers which enabled the grower to have 'PURE AIR DRIED' stamped on his pockets. The products of combustion from the fire were led through a number of iron pipes before escaping to the chimneys. These pipes were in the 'plenum' chamber below the hops and warmed the hop-drying air as it moved up through them.

Ted Shew, a grower from Cold Green, Bosbury, installed many Shew's Patent ovens made by Jones and Attwood, the manufacturers of greenhouse heating equipment in Stourbridge. The air was forced through the hops by a fan in the bottom of the kiln, unlike the Joyce's Patent where the air was sucked through by a fan in the top. W. Wargent and Sons of Stoke Edith bought Joyce's Patent in 1920, and had a great deal of success after improving the design by enclosing the pipes. In one year they installed thirty. It was reckoned that hops dried by Joyce's Patent won more prizes at exhibitions because the fan above the hops was more efficient at removing the reek from the top layers. Later, automatic underfeed stokers were added, fuel hoppers which fed anthracite to the bottom of the ovens. These were controlled electrically by Oto Control, a development of W. J. Wargent, the senior partner. Oto Control kept a predetermined rate of temperature increase and the same system is in use today, controlling oil burners.

A Mr Partridge, who grew hops at Wharton Court, near Leominster, was responsible for importing Sirocco driers from Belfast. Originally designed for tea drying they had very powerful fans. Neil Parker at Newton Farm, Stoke Lacy, has one of these blowing air through a tunnel which is able to dry three kilns simultaneously, although it has now been converted to oil burning with a Jones Rotomiser installation.

Since the Second World War most drying has changed over to gas oil fuel with self-contained electrically driven fans, driving the air from under the load.

Farmer Pudge of New House, Bishops Frome, had several of the Urquhart make installed before the war. Since then the most popular has been the Nu-Way, built at Droitwich. This has the advantage of a very high airspeed fan which drives warm air through the hops at speeds of 50 or 60 ft per minute in some cases. Previously 25 ft per minute was a reasonable airspeed. High airspeeds allow deeper loading of hops if required, or a shorter period of low temperature drying, which allows the total drying time to be the same, but at a lower maximum temperature, perhaps 140 degrees F or less. Consequently the quality is better.

Hops dried by oilfired burners cannot generally be classed as pure air dried because the air is drawn directly through the flame to the hops; but as there is total combustion (which is not the case with solid fuel) there is no danger of contamination unless the burner is set incorrectly and pure diesel oil goes through the hops. If this happens the contamination is obvious from the smell. The hops have to be immediately disposed of as waste. Direct air drying has the advantage of fast automatic reaction to changes in the ambient atmosphere. This is essential with the high airspeeds.

Safety is another factor much improved by the modern self-contained oil burners. Before electricity was generally available fans were driven by shafts and belts from internal combustion engines or tractor pulleys. It was impossible to guard these shafts adequately and sometimes greensacks would have to be unloaded in the vicinity of rotating shafts, necessary because they provided the drive to another kiln which was already loaded. Indeed, on an external drive a man was once trapped and killed and his body found later still rotating on the shaft.

A roller hair kiln at New House, Bishops Frome. The handle being turned by the man on the right caused the roller hair under the hops to roll forward to the kiln outlet and deposit the hops on to the carrying sheet.

It has been recognised since the last century that the warm air leaving the kiln in an unsaturated state represented an inefficient use of energy. To make use of this waste warm air multi-tiered systems of drying have been introduced. In the simplest two-tier system, as practised in a converted kiln at Richard Bradstock's of Ashperton, hops are first loaded from greensacks onto the top kiln floor, which is made up of perforated plattens which can be tilted open by levers to allow the load to drop through to the lower drying floor. The top floor is again loaded and drying begins, the warm exhaust air from the lower bed being forced up through the plattens to start to dry the upper bed. When the lower bed is dry the hops are removed in carrying bins and the partly dried upper bed is dropped through the plattens and the upper floor reloaded with green hops. The burner can then continue almost immediately at its maximum permitted temperature because there will be very little moisture left to condense in the air from the lower floor, the hops having already been partly dried. Three loads a day are usually done in this manner but if necessary these operations can be carried out continuously with a sufficient supply of hops.

Bigger growers, such as Peter Walker of Knightwick, have kilns with three tiers. Hops are unloaded automatically off an elevator into platten-bottomed bins before being moved into the drying area. The second drop releases them into lighter built bins which are removed and tipped onto the cooling floor by hand. Only three men are needed to operate four of these 20 ft square kilns, working from 7.00 a.m. to 9.00 p.m. and 55 pockets a day can be managed comfortably. Using greensacks on the old single-tier system nine men were necessary. R. M. Capper of the Stocks, Suckley, who was the first in the country to have three-tier drying with completely automatic loading saved 40% of drying fuel in the first year.

Diagram showing the effect of improved mechanisation on labour utilisation at Ankerdine Farm.

Peter Walker

		Picking staff	Kiln staff
1954	4 Picking machines + 4 Sets of Kilns	🚶	🚶
1968	2 Picking machines together. + 2 Sets of Kilns.	🚶	🚶
1980	2 Picking machines together. + 1 Set of Kilns.	🚶	🚶

Some modern drying systems employ bins. These are being pushed into the drying chamber after being loaded with hops ready for the first stage of three-tier drying.

After the first stage of drying, plattens are opened in the bottom of the bin to allow the hops to drop through to the tier below for the next stage.

In order to release hops from the second stage to the nylon mesh bins seen behind the open flaps at floor level, handles have to be operated from the cooling floor to open the plattens of the second tier.

Hops can be inspected by withdrawing the nylon bins of the bottom tier and returning to the drying chamber if necessary. These bins are light enough to be carried and tipped by two men.

At Moreton Jeffries, John Cotton has a three-tier Wolf drier made in Germany and installed by CWF Ltd of Ledbury, who added a fourth tier above the others on to which the hops from the picker are unloaded by an operator controlled elevator. The plattens on this loading tier are not perforated so the exhaust air has to be released through the side of the kiln between the two top tiers in order that the operator has a reasonable working atmosphere. John is well aware of the savings in fuel he is making from this system as he has a flow meter in the burner feed. About six gallons per zentner of dried hops is consumed. 5.7 gallons was burnt in the best year, but on the old single-tier system half as much fuel again was used.

The ultimate in three-tier drying has been erected at Allied Breweries Ltd hop farm at Brierley Court. Hops are subjected to 'production line' treatment, controlled by pressing buttons. They are first carried on a wire mesh belt over a cold air chamber, originally designed for sulphuring hops. This practice was banned in the year of manufacture, but the air prevents the hops sweating and discolouring, as they are apt to in bulk, particularly if drying is delayed, and there is a bonus in that the moisture driven off by the cold air is sufficient to cause a significant saving of fuel. Hops then pass over the three mesh-belt tiers of the Wolf discontinuous drier: each time the bottom tier is dry each mesh moves forward, depositing its load on the one beneath, which is extended in order to catch the hops and travels in the opposite direction. Although fuelled by oil this is arranged so that it is heated by pure air. On leaving the drier, hops are carried over a 'conditioning' chamber which is only used to apply a little more hot air if the drier has not done the job precisely enough. From here the next stop is the automatic weigher and baler, and hops are then ready for delivery to the brewery. Two of these units dry 260 acres of hops picked by two Super E Bruff Machines.

Rosemaund E.H.F. and Wye College have played a prominent part in the development of a very cheap method of fuel saving by re-circulation of air. All that is needed is a duct outside the kiln to carry exhaust air from above the hops to the fan heater inlet. This is opened when the exhaust air humidity is beginning to decrease, about halfway through drying, and with judicious operation 15% saving has been achieved. Three farms in the area used this system in 1984.

Hop Processing

Hops still leave the farm in the cylindrical pocket or rectangular bale but a new industry has now been developed between the kilns and the brewery to process them into more convenient forms for the users. Hop Developments Limited took over the well-known old local hop farm, the Moor Farm at Eardiston in the Teme Valley, and converted it into a factory for refining, powdering and pelleting hops into 'Hopstabil Pellets'. These are vacuum packed and take up much less room than pockets or bales. Pellets can be a blend of different varieties of aroma and/or alpha hops and produced at a specified alpha percentage at the instructions of the brewer.

Hop Developments Ltd also have at Eardiston a pilot CO_2 (carbon dioxide) extraction plant which uses the most efficient process yet devised to extract the required brewing substances from the hop.

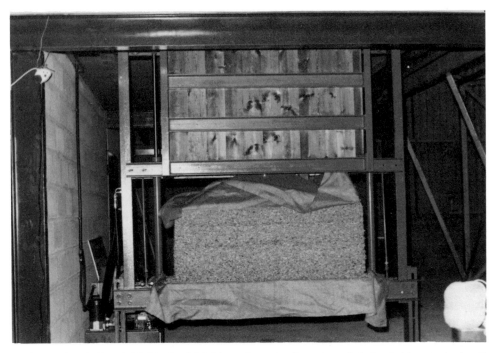

Modern hop baling. This block of dried hops from the floor above is being held under hydraulic pressure ready for the hessian cloths to be sewn round it with an electric stitcher.

Sulphuring

Before the 1970s, samples displaying a very green coloured bract were very unpopular, possibly because it indicated immaturity. This was the main reason for sparse nitrogen manuring by some growers. Nowadays the main reason for sparing the nitrogen is the expense, and the greater danger of wilt, for merchants' tastes have changed and green hops are no longer so despised.

It was found that burning roll sulphur under hops at the beginning of drying would bleach out some of the green colour, and Dr Burgess, the renowned hop scientist, even worked out a formula based on airspeed through the load, ripeness and dampness, for the quantity to be used. Some people would apply a late dusting of powder sulphur to the growing crop not only as a mould eradicant, but in the hope that it would act as a bleach if it became wet. It all seemed a load of codswallop to me because I could not see any difference in colour between a sulphured and an unsulphured hop. It paid however because a properly sulphured hop was always valued higher. The late Michael Jackson, a director of the old factoring firm, Selmes, Jackson and Gulland, always held my respect because we used to take samples to him at Worcester Hop Fair and he could grade as many as six differently sulphured samples in order according to the amount of sulphur we had burnt under them, and give advice as to which quantity was the optimum.

Nobody liked using sulphur. It permeated the kilns for half an hour or more after loading and all the grass, and sometimes the farm gardens near the kilns, would be killed by it long before acid rain was ever thought of. The late Les Hinds, the Bromyard builder, who used to help Hubert Baker and Jim Walton in the kilns at Little Froome, told me of an unpleasant experience when the fans in the tops of the kilns were driven by a single cylinder diesel engine. Apparently, this type of machine, towards the end of the week when it had become well and truly hot, could be started merely by turning the flywheel by hand. The kiln had just been loaded and Jim went in to ignite the sulphur with a horseshoe made red hot in the Joyce's oven while the other two went out to start the engine to drive the fan. Unfortunately, when hot, the engine would also run backwards if accidentally started in that direction and that is what happened, without them realising. The fan therefore drove the sulphur back into the kiln resting area, where they found poor old Jim collapsed, and had to drag him out, luckily with no serious harm done.

Oil burners have no stove in which to heat horseshoes so in those kilns methylated spirits was poured into the sulphur pans for ignition. A very tragic event occurred near Ledbury a few years ago when a young man accidentally dropped a bottle of methylated spirits in a kiln. It burst on the floor, splashed all over him, ignited and caused burns so serious that he died.

At the Brewing Research Foundation at Nuffield it had been found that the bittering value of hops contaminated with sulphur was reduced, and also that sulphur 'off-tastes' could sometimes be identified in the beer by tasting panels. The brewers asked the Hops Marketing Board to ban the use of sulphur in the kilns in 1980 and, in spite of the fact that valuation had previously been improved, everybody was pleased to be rid of it. In fact, growers no longer dust hops with sulphur against mould after burr because even that can cause contamination.

All Faults

This is a subject which is not discussed in the best hop circles because 'it does not exist', and I have found it very difficult to come by any information. Of course I have no personal experience of it. It appears that sometimes hops are not properly dried. The skilled drier removes his hops from the kiln at such a finely judged stage that the slightest maltreatment or carelessness between then and bagging can cause the hops to retain or absorb too much moisture and they will 'perish', exuding a bad, cheesy smell on exposure. They are then useless. If not spotted before entering the warehouse where they are weighed, and samples are drawn, the weight return for the afflicted pocket will be endorsed with the dread initials A.F. for All Faults. Affected pockets can be identified before leaving the kilns by sticking a sharp pocket knife, inclined upwards, into them. If the knife slices through the hops on forcing the handle upwards, the pocket is sound, but if the hops are 'cold' or improperly cured, they are almost impossible to cut. The degree of fault can be ascertained by inserting the probes of a megger and all pockets in the warehouses are so tested. Hop factors visit the kilns during picking to check on conditions and always carry a megger, but growers themselves are tending to obtain the instruments nowadays.

All kinds of tricks have been tried when cold pockets have been discovered, all of them illegal under the old Hops Marketing Board rules. The simplest was to put the pocket into the plenum chamber at a temperature of 140° F or above, and apparently, with borderline cases, this was successful. A really bad pocket would have to be emptied and redried. I believe some driers developed great skill in repacking afterwards so that the treatment was not apparent. The secret was not to press the hops so much in the bottom of the pocket as in the top. Nowadays it is not illegal to treat cold pockets and it is much simpler and easier. Borough Hop Traders Ltd at Thinghill Court have a chamber which freeze-dries complete pockets with no need for any other disturbance.

Sampling

Between hop picking and December, rectangular block samples of the dried, compressed hops are cut from the pockets through the side seams, and sent to the factors' showrooms for valuation and display to the merchants. The showrooms used to be in the Borough area of London but have now moved to Paddock Wood in Kent. Originally these used to be illuminated by skylights, but London smog could darken the interiors so much that on some days valuation (which even today depends to a large extent on the brightness and colour of the hop) would be impossible. Eventually, and after much experiment, a special artificial lighting system was introduced, which was also installed in the Paddock Wood showrooms after the move.

Hops were not on display only for merchants: the showrooms were the only opportunity for the grower to see the results of his yearlong labour as a coherent entity, and to study the final effects of his management, which could then be altered or improved as necessary. Thus it became obligatory for all good growers to spend at least one day in winter in London. Pubs, clubs and shows were ancillary. Factors were, and still are, always extremely hospitable, although in the old unenlightened days when the grower was not supposed to know the merchant who bought his hops, and certainly not the brewer who actually used them, ingenious ploys would occasionally have to be resorted to in order to prevent the meeting of the parties.

CHAPTER 12

Marketing Yesterday and Today

'Hops a good deal cultivated, and chiefly disposed of to British dealers.'

John Claudius Louden, 1783-1843.

One of the many problems for hop growers is that there is only one significant buyer—the brewer.

In Victorian times hops were used extensively for preserving baking yeast when bread was made from hops, yeast, raisins and flour, and only recently the Worcester hop merchant, Richard Rayer, has had enquiries from Bombay for the same purpose. ISO-compounds derived from alpha acids, which are responsible for much of the bittering and antiseptic power of the hop, are peculiar in that their toxicity is effective against many bacteria, but not against yeasts. Victorian ships all had to carry hops for yeast preservation, and Pike, a London merchant used to have the Admiralty Contract until the early 1950s. In the late 20th century navy, however, hops only find their way on board ship in the beer.

During the First World War hops were used by the Germans as an adulteration to eke out tobacco, and before the war it was quite common to eat the spring shoots like asparagus. Geoffrey Loyd, the herbal horticulturist from Ocle Pychard, started re-encouraging this culinary cannabic craving in 1984 and was successful in selling shoots to Harrods', and Fortnum and Masons' restaurants in London. Other growers have been exploiting hops in this way since, and Rosemaund E.H.F. is studying the situation. Hops have also recently been used to make cheese manufactured from ewe's milk more palatable by maturing it for two months in barrels of hops, thereby instilling a uniquely pleasant flavour. Unfortunately these outlets do not have sufficient potential to justify the capital necessary to grow the crop, and they can only produce a little pocket money from existing facilities during situations of surplus.

The success of the hop industry therefore depends on the brewing industry but it is not a direct straight line relationship with the level of beer production. U.K. beer consumption per head has decreased from 248 pints per year at the beginning of the century to 194 pints in 1983, although total production is about the same at almost 37 million barrels having dropped to 18 million barrels in 1932. On the other hand the hop acreage over the same period has declined to a quarter, from 51,308 acres to 12,577, although in Herefordshire itself the decline is only about a half, from 7,287 acres to 3,576, this discrepancy in the ratio being due mainly to the virulence of progressive verticillium wilt in the South East since 1924.

The original factor leading to this decline was a change in taste to a lighter beer using less hops. The hopping rate per barrel of 36 imperial gallons decreased from about 5 lbs in the middle of the last century to 1.84 lbs before 1910, 1.31 lbs in the

'30s, 0.91 lbs in the '40s, and is even believed to have been as low as 0.14 lbs. Latterly the decline has been due more to technical advances by the brewers, and the higher alpha acid varieties of hops bred by Professors Salmon and Neve at Wye College.

During the First World War a build up of hop stocks considered sufficient for four years occurred, so the government ordered farmers to cut their acreages to 50% of the 1914 area. On Armistice Day they were immediately allowed to replant up to 75% of the 1914 area but there was a reluctance to do so because of the high cost of wirework.

Importation of hops had to be allowed and then in 1920 the beer tax was increased from 70/- to 100/- per barrel, which had the effect of converting a severe hop shortage into a staggering surfeit within the space of twelve months.

Also other factors have combined to lessen the quantity of beer drunk per head. The licensing laws introduced with the object of keeping the country working more efficiently during the First World War were never repealed and modern leisure pursuits, the cinema and later television, left people less drinking hours anyway. Mechanisation has abolished many really heavy jobs in industry and agriculture, and with them the necessity to replace millions of gallons of sweat with millions of gallons of beer. The more recent drinking and driving laws have not helped either, although there are many ways of overcoming the obstacles engendered without being a danger to anyone else.

With all these difficulties it is a wonder there was a past for hops in this century, let alone a future. Stability was originally maintained by the Hop Control Scheme set up in August 1917 and run by the Hop Controller, Mr Foster Clark, and a management committee of members from the Board of Agriculture, growers, factors, merchants and brewers. This body dissolved in 1925 leaving growers in a difficult position, with a surplus of 100,000 cwts of hops, but the comparative stability under Hop Control gave them confidence to set up a voluntary, elected body of their own, English Hop Growers Ltd. The 'pooling' system was continued, in which all payments for hops were paid into a central pool from which growers were remunerated. Unfortunately continuing surpluses, and the few growers who stayed outside English Hop Growers Ltd., breaking its power of unity, were sufficient to make things impossible, and in 1929 the company was wound up. However, the Agricultural Marketing Act of 1931 made it possible for growers to set up a compulsory marketing board in 1932 which every hop grower had to join. The general trading system was altered as little as possible: the hop factors who had previously been the farmers' agents and were responsible for sampling and showing the hops to merchants and brewers, as well as advising growers, became agents to the Hops Marketing Board with much the same responsibility, and merchants continued to select hops on behalf of brewers. The new arrangements saved the situation and were aided in the first two years by a demand in excess of supply.

A letter to a brewery in August 1932 from John Essex Potter of Stanford Court shows his reaction to the Board:

'Dear Sir,

I am writing to ask if you would like to have my growth of hops this year as you have been doing in the past; and to say how much I should like you to do so.

Of course I am compelled to send them to the Hops Marketing Board; but I understand that you will have the option of taking them as in the past. I am told that, under the new arrangement, the factor will sell the hops (as Agents of the Board) direct to Brewers, who can, if they so choose, appoint any merchant, or merchants, to act as their Agents and to advise them, but at the same time the contracts for sale and purchase will be between the Brewers and the Marketing Board.

I have an excellent growth this year again, but Monday's gale has whipped and bruised the hops badly everywhere.

The Factors who will have my hops (with the exception of twenty pockets) will be my old Factors who handled the growth for me previous to my selling the growth direct to you. They are Messrs. Noakes & Banister of 45 Borough High Street, London, S.E.1. The 20 pockets, which I have mentioned, will go to Messrs. Wild Neame & Coy also of Borough High Street, S.E.1.

I think that, in order to make sure that you have the offer of my hops, it may be well for you to write the Marketing Board claiming the first refusal of them.

If you like to come and see the growth before picking I shall be very pleased to meet you Wed or Thursday at W'ster.

Yours faithfully,

Quotas were introduced in 1934, to prevent growers selling more than their fair share of hops through the Board in seasons of glut. A basic quota in weight was allotted to each farm, based on previous quantities grown, and, after determining the likely demand from discussions with the Brewers' Society, early each year the Board would specify the Annual Quota for that season as a percentage of Basic. The percentage could be increased later in the year if the sales position became more optimistic (once it was increased by 6% as late as the middle of hop picking when it became known that the German crop had suffered severely from mould) but growers were only paid the full rate on the weight of the annual quota issued. Unless a grower with surplus was able to obtain extra quota from one with a short crop, his surplus hops, if he picked them, would be consigned to a pool of non-quota account and would probably only receive a small proportion of the quota account valuation.

The monopoly powers of the Hops Marketing Board and the Brewers' Society agreement to accept all English hops on a cost plus basis enabled the Board to control acreage when necessary. The hop price was based on average growing costs plus a percentage profit, and growers were selected at random every year to have different aspects thoroughly costed in order to determine a true average. The costs covered the complete acreage grown whether picked or not, so in a year when hops were 'let fly' because too many were grown, brewers were in effect paying for unpicked goods and put pressure on the Board to reduce the acreage grown. This occurred in 1966. Although beer production was quietly increasing, hopping rate* was decreasing to such an extent that less acreage was necessary. In

*hopping rate—the rate at which hops are added to beer, for instance 1 lb per barrel.

the following two years the HMB imposed a levy of £2.14s.0d. per cental (100 lb dried hops) which was used to buy out any growers willing to give up altogether. They were paid up to £900 per ton for their basic quota according to the proportion of annual quota grown in previous years, and altogether 86 producers gave up and grubbed 1,837 acres, a decrease of 11.7% in two years. This enabled the basic quota of the remainder to be increased by 9.8%.

Upon the United Kingdom joining the Common Market in February 1973, there was no longer a quantitative import control of hops from Europe so marketing had to begin to adapt to foreign trading habits to be competitive. This meant the end of the cost plus system and hops had to be offered several years ahead as was already the Continental custom. Previously if insufficient hops of a variety required by a brewer were available the buyer would accept a substitute, but this was no longer acceptable. Thus hops were offered ahead, by variety, at a fixed price. However the 1976 crop was the first when growers had the unique consolation of an inflation surcharge based on a formula operating from the year of offer.

Beer production continued to increase and English hop acreage to decrease during the '70s due to falling demand for hops occasioned by increased acreage of high alpha varieties. The Hereford and Worcester acreage declined from 6,781 in 1966 to 5,520 in 1976. The figures kindly produced by Peter Walker are typical,

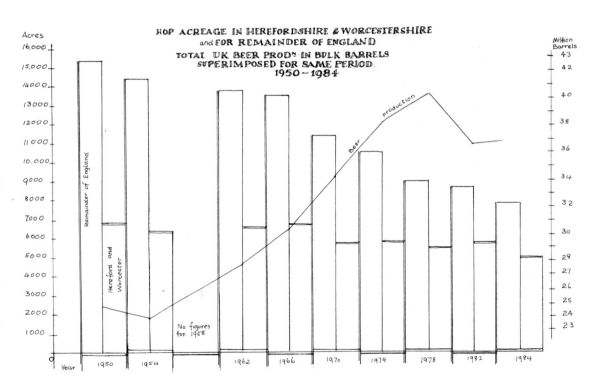

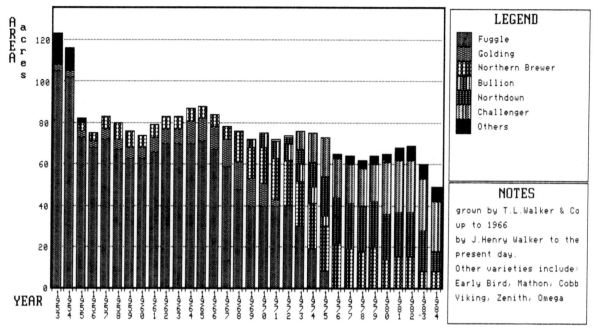

Diagram of acreages of hops at Ankerdine Farm 1953-84, showing changes in the varieties of hops grown.

and also show that 1976 was the first year he grew only alpha varieties, having grubbed his Fuggles the previous year and Goldings in 1971. Falling demand and general world overproduction induced the EEC to impose an order prohibiting expansion of hop area in the Community between 1 July 1977 and 31 December 1979. Although this order was obeyed, even in the Bromyard area, and many hops were also grubbed, the wirework was often left standing and immediately replanted when the order ceased.

The EEC has certainly made life different for the English grower by forcing the abolition of the HMB although the loss of insularity is to a certain extent ameliorated by annual income aid based on acreage and variety of hops. But the basic reason for the very real difficulty hop growers are in at the moment is world overproduction which is a problem whether we are in the Common Market or not. It is compounded by the unusually large stocks of hops being held by brewers, a situation due partly to the production of extracts which can be kept much longer than the unmanufactured product. Growers hope that supply and demand may be more in equilibrium by 1988 at the latest, but since 1979 British beer production itself has actually been declining—fortunately it is still 150% of 1950 output.

The Hereford and Worcester area has decreased from 6,860 acres in 1950 to 4,786 acres in 1984. The only consolation to be gleaned from the figures is that we have shrunk proportionately less than the rest of the country. In 1950 we grew 31% of the total acreage and in 1984 it was 38%. This is probably mainly due to the ravages of verticillium wilt in Kent. We are presently having great difficulty in containing the disease in this part of the country and it behoves everyone to take every possible precaution against its spread.

Eventually the EEC decreed that the Hops Marketing Board, being a monopoly, was illegal, and in April 1982 it formed itself into a voluntary body, the Hops Marketing Board Limited, changing its name again in April 1985 to English Hops Limited.

The abolition of the monopoly and compulsory powers of the Hops Marketing Board gave growers freedom to sell how they liked and without reference to the Board, if they so pleased. Pooling would no longer be enforced. This comparative freedom, like the freedom to smoke, has turned out to be a danger to the health of the body. Fortunately, in the case of the English hop industry, I believe this danger has been now overcome after several years of extremely diligent activity by the directors in sounding out the diverse views of the members, and much patient argument and compromise, particularly over pooling. It had become especially important for growers to consider each other as well as themselves, because the total number of growers in England had declined to less than 320.

British brewers have generally preferred to obtain hops from the same farm every year although in many cases, due to the way the factoring and merchanting system worked, the grower himself was unaware of the final destination of his product, except perhaps, when a rude letter would arrive from a brewery complaining about foreign bodies, such as pieces of hop-picking machine, being packed with the hops. The brewer had the first chance of the next year's hops off the same farm—this was known as the 'courtesy call'. Some growers objected to sharing the proceeds of their crop with the rest of the 'pool' because, according to their point of view, if their hops were wanted enough to attract the courtesy call year after year they could very well be more valuable than others in the pool and yet they were only receiving the same price—the Customer is Always Right! Of course those growers, if the system was altered, had to be prepared to make a poor sale, or perhaps no sale at all if for some reason their customer changed his mind.

The matter is now settled with a few growers 'going it alone', a few more forming small independent selling groups, but the majority deciding to remain full members of English Hops Ltd as the Hops Marketing Board has been reconstituted.

In English Hops Ltd only one variety, Wye Target, will be compulsorily pooled. This is because it is a high alpha hop very suitable for the export market and can be sold on the basis of alpha acid content. Very few of this variety are yet grown in the Bromyard area because they are wilt tolerant and, until a farm is suffering extremely severely from the disease, may not be grown. For all other varieties growers will receive the actual price agreed individually with factors or merchants, less of course commission and English Hops Ltd's expenses. These expenses cover sampling, grading, warehousing and market information. The company will also be responsible for distributing EEC hop subsidies and the collection of payments for research and development which along with a similar substantial donation from the Brewers Society and also, we hope, the Government and other interested agencies will be used to fund research at Wye College, East Malling, and other establishments. This research and development donation is essential to enable the English hop industry to succeed against extremely keen world competition.

The big problem now left facing English growers is over supply and storage of hops on a world scale. The only answer to this is grubbing and to be effective needs to be carried out internationally. Unfortunately, each hop-growing country thinks that the others ought to do it, so economic forces will eventually impose the solution.

Wm. Ed. Le May, Dudley Le May, M.C., Stafford Le May, Leslie Le May.

Hop Factors

1872—1949.

RELIABILITY AND SERVICE

W. H. & H. LeMAY

67, BOROUGH HIGH STREET,

LONDON, S.E.1.

('Phone : Hop 1945 & 1946).

Enquiries to Mr. NORMAN H. Le MAY, Hop Pole Hotel, Bromyard (Phone Bromyard 49).

The Bromyard News & Record, 8 September 1949.

HOPS

When morning mists in Autumn, weave patterns in the vale,
And heavy dews that hint at frost, the lush green meadows pale;
And sheaves of corn in barn and rick, declare the harvest home,
Men still have hops to gather, down by the River Froome.

From many a smoke drenched city, from many a dreary slum,
From many a gaunt Welsh mining town, the pale faced families come,
By train and bus to Ledbury Town, excited, noisy, gay,
The happiest time in their drab lives—a holiday with pay.

Along the roads of England, from Lancashire to Kent,
Across the lonely mountain tracks, of Cumbria and Gwent,
The gypsy vans with yellow sides, red wheels, tarpaulin tops,
Are hurrying down to Bishop's Froome, to pick the golden hops.

As soon as chill September morn is warmed by mounting sun,
Deserted vans and barns denote that picking has begun;
In yards where golden bosses shine, against the broad green leaves,
Cascading from the taut straight wire, to which each tendril cleaves.

The serried, shady, dark green aisles, so orderly since May,
Become untidy heaps of bine, increasing day by day,
Till pole and wire stand bare and gaunt, against the Autumn sky,
From Withington to Ledbury Town, from Hegdon Hill to Wye.

Throughout the month, while picking lasts, that tranquil countryside,
Becomes a hive of industry, from morn to eventide;
From field to kiln the wagons go, piled high with bags of hops,
There's bustle in the farmer's house, and in the village shops.

At length the fragrant blooms are safe, the yearly task is o'er,
And on the farms round Ledbury Town, each barn becomes a store
Of pockets, ranged in long straight rows, like soldiers on parade,
The oast-house fires have been withdrawn, the noisy pickers paid.

The city dwellers have returned, to smoke and grime again,
Those faces, pale a month ago, now tanned by sun and rain—
The gypsy vans have headed West, along the road to Wales,
To pitch their camps in wooded dells, before the winter gales.

'Tis quiet now round Ledbury Town, there's peace in Bishop's Froome,
Tis silent now in barn and byre, and in the farmer's home,
The final act that ends the scene, as daylight hours decline,
Are winking fires in hop yards, where men are burning bine.

Geoffrey Bright, *Hereford is Heaven*, 1948.

APPENDIX

1. Table showing the acreage of hops grown in each parish within a 6 mile radius of Bromyard 1807-1985.

Year	1807	1810	1815	1820	1825	1830	1835	1840	1845	1850	1855	1860	1870	1880	1890	1900	1910	1916	1925	1935	1945	1955	1965	1975	1985
Acton Beauchamp	160	150	137	159	150	122	132	98	74	53	61	43	63	76	73	82	84	88	60	70	63	62	65	52	106
Avenbury	246	240	241	257	240	200	238	243	167	99	118	102	39	148	116	126	90	74	89	96	87	117	100	77	56
Bishops Frome	375	348	381	401	459	336	430	299	261	166	200	164	68	216	245	341	261	220	326	238	285	231	201	172	197
Bredenbury	60	61	59	62	56	70	32	26	27	20	19	13	6	10	11	6	3	0	0	0	0	0	0	0	0
*Bromyard	660	650	507	668	630	602	734	416	332	198	230	162	222	113	116	105	66	41	7	11	5	4	0	0	0
Collington	64	60	69	67	67	60	65	52	36	23	37	23	13	27	39	15	9	0	0	0	0	17	35	35	21
Cradley	274	294	286	364	145	277	365	184	166	138	162	154	216	234	270	330	285	205	159	185	185	160	160	94	103
Docklow	104	120	101	95	118	130	117	66	83	52	47	50	14	62	47	35	18	21	8	3	0	0	0	0	0
Edvin Loach	24	29	21	21	21	24	13	16	18	11	15	9	5			11	9	0	0	0	0	0	0	0	0
Edwyn Ralph	110	98	96	106	105	102	96	60	37	40	55	30	32	29	17	14	2	0	0	0	0	0	0	0	0
Evesbatch	34	38	52	57	67	60	73	38	43	33	34	31		33	45	35	10	14	7	6	8	6	21	29	23
Grendon Bishop	105	98	80	101	110	80	101	96	55	44	47	42	42	68	35	25	3	0	89	0	0	0	0	0	0
Hatfield	0	0	0	0	83	40	96	0	0	0	44	27	43	39	62	18	0	2	0	0	0	4	0	0	0
Little Cowarne	91	80	84	88	169	196	85	50	39	26	31	20	30	33	23	26	11	4	8	6	9	7	0	0	0
Moreton Jeffries													31	37	42	47	43	45	51	49	59	49	67	70	45
Much Cowarne	81	84	60	78	221	230	230	207	185	143	137	101	152	177	157	172	139	134	172	205	223	231	176	102	103
Pencombe/Grendon Warren	228	248	238	356	350	362	335	242	177	118	144	77	102	81	72	51	9	5	8	50	10	27	30	0	33
Stanford Bishop	147	149	141	171	215	36	128	101	79	56	57	46	65	57	64	54	56	5	50	50	50	27	30	37	33
Stoke Lacy	159	180	118	215	125	196	157	93	86	57	60	62	95	88	146	131	69	44	55	46	48	64	69	52	28
Tedstone Delamere	161	143	118	135	125	80	118	95	63	53	61	42	54	40	28	10	0	0	0	0	0	0	0	0	0
Tedstone Wafer												8	8	2	8	10	4	3	0	0	0	0	0	0	0
Thornbury	131	144	141	138	141	109	123	106	80	56	54	54	72	58	80	73	9	16	0	0	0	0	0	0	0
Ullingswick	0	0	0	0	107	80	60	55	46	31	42	33	65	50	81	100	75	68	41	43	46	32	28	31	8
Upper Sapey	90	144	105	76	119	104	126	55	45	30	69	69	29	47	21	22	13	3	0	0	0	0	0	0	0
Wacton	91	100	101	88	90	100	79	22	0	0	24	15	15	22	15	20	0	0	5	0	0	0	0	0	0
Whitbourne	400	406	307	394	258	248	255	159	132	115	131	107	142	94	111	133	109	71	67	45	45	12	12	10	10
Wolferlow	44	54	60	60	55	60	63	54	40	41	5	20	39	28	71	57	10	10	5	0	0	0	0	0	0
Total acreage	3839	3918	3568	4109	4246	3904	4251	2833	2271	1603	1884	1480	1662	1869	1995	2045	1387	1122	1202	1063	1123	1028	964	761	733

*Including Linton, Norton and Winslow

Where blank spaces occur in the table the figures have not been traced.

Sources: Excise Lists, British Library

Crop Returns, Public Record Office

English Hops Ltd.

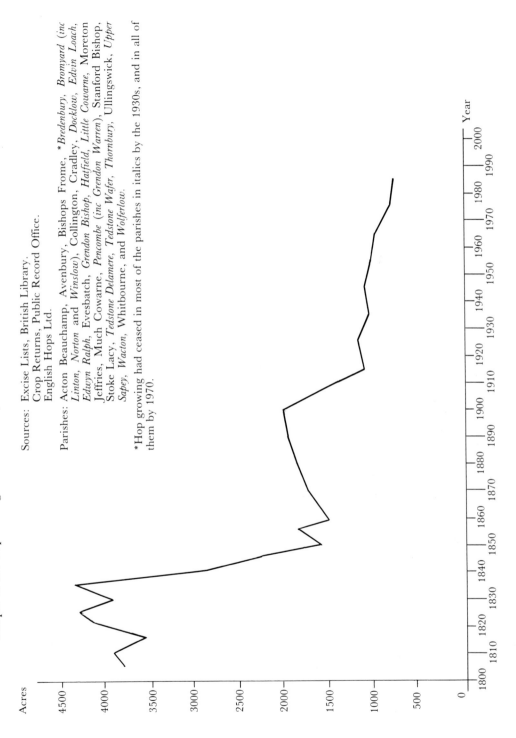

Graph of the hop acreage in the Bromyard District 1807-1985, based on the table opposite.

Sources: Excise Lists, British Library.
Crop Returns, Public Record Office.
English Hops Ltd.

Parishes: Acton Beauchamp, Avenbury, Bishops Frome, *Bredenbury, Bromyard (inc Linton, Norton and Winslow), Collington, Cradley, Docklow, Edvin Loach, Edvyn Ralph, Evesbatch, Grendon Bishop, Hatfield, Little Cowarne, Moreton Jeffries, Much Cowarne, Pencombe (inc Grendon Warren), Stanford Bishop, Stoke Lacy, Tedstone Delamere, Tedstone Wafer, Thornbury, Ullingswick, Upper Sapey, Wacton, Whitbourne, and Wolferlow.

*Hop growing had ceased in most of the parishes in italics by the 1930s, and in all of them by 1970.

2. Table showing varieties of hops grown within a 6 mile radius of Bromyard 1955-1985.

	No. of farms growing hops	No. of farms growing Fuggles	Acreage of Fuggles	No. of farms growing Goldings	Acreage of Goldings	No. of farms growing Wye Challenger	Acreage of Wye Challenger	No. of farms growing Wye Northdown	Acreage of Wye Northdown	No. of farms growing other new varieties	Acreage of other new varieties	Total acreage new varieties	Total acreage of hops
1955	68	67	970	12	56					1	1.5	1.5	1028
1965	54	54	890	14	70					2	3.1	3.1	964
1975	42	34	359	10	46					35	*356	*356	761
1985	36	30	318	9	61	24	146	22	195	7	13	354	733

*These figures were not differentiated by the Hops Marketing Board

3. Table showing the relative acreages of the English hop-growing regions 1955-1985.

	1955	1965	1975	1985
West Midlands	6358	6818	5681	4413
% of total	31%	33%	36%	38%
Farms within 6 mile radius of Bromyard	1028	963	761	733
South and South East	14100	13869	10082	7312
Total acreage	20458	20687	15763	11725

From the above figures it can be calculated that whereas in 1985 the total acreage was 57% of the 1955 figure, and in the West Midlands itself the 1985 acreage was 69% of the 1955 area, the farms within a 6 mile radius of Bromyard had maintained as much as 71% of their hop-growing acreage over the same period.

How appropriate today is John Beale's comment made 300 years ago when he claimed that with the growth of hops around Bromyard, '.... we make haste to be the chief Hop-masters in England'!

BIBLIOGRAPHY

1   Arnold, Richard, *The Customs of London* (1502).
2   Beale, John, *Herefordshire Orchards—A pattern for all England* (1656).
3   *Berrow's Worcester Journal.*
4   Board of Agriculture Leaflet no 55, *The Swallow* (1904).
5   *Bromyard Deanery Magazine* (1901, 1902, 1905).
6   *Bromyard News and Record*, Bromyard Library.
7   Burgess, A. H., *Hops Botany Cultivation and Utilisation* (1964).
8   Clinch, George, *English Hops* (1919).
9   Defoe, Daniel, *A Tour Through Britain* (1724).
10 Filmer, Richard, *Hops and hop picking* (1982).
11 French, R. K., *The History and Virtues of Cyder* (1982).
12 Gaut, R. C., *A History of Worcestershire Agriculture & Rural Evolution* (1939).
13 *Hereford Journal*, Hereford Library.
14 Jones, E. L. and Moss, N., *Report on the Experimental Work on Hops* (1959).
15 Kent, Nathaniel, *Hints to Gentlemen of Landed Property* (1793).
16 Lance, E. J., *The Hop Farmer* (1838).
17 *The Leominster Guide* (1808).
18 Loudon, J. C., *Loudon's Encyclopaedia of Agriculture* (1835).
19 Lowden, S., *The Locational Change of Hop Farming in Herefordshire*, Aberystwyth University (1981).
20 Scot, Reynolde, *A Perfite Platforme of a Hoppe Garden* (1574).
21 *Slater's Directory*, (1859).
22 Stephens, Henry, *The Book of the Farm* (1851).
23 *Swithun Butterfield's Survey*, ff 129 (1577).
24 Tusser, Thomas, *Five Hundred Points of Good Husbandry* (1573).
25 Webb, J., *Memorials of the Civil War in Herefordshire* (1879).
26 *The Young Woman's Companion or Female Instructor* (c1800).

MAPS

The Hereford Record Office holds two series (incomplete) of maps useful for tracing old hopyards:

1. The parish tithe maps and apportionments for the 1830s-40s.
2. Hop Maps AS78/1-75 (Herefordshire) and AS78/76-124 (Worcestershire) for the 1950s-60s recently deposited by English Hops Ltd.

GLOSSARY

acaricide	chemical used for killing red spider
alecost	costmary (*chrysanthemum balsamita tanacetoides*)
alehoof	ground ivy (*glechoma hederacea*)
aphids	insect pests
bagging hole	*see* treading hole
bait	food for break time
barrage balloon	large tethered balloon to deter low-flying aircraft
beethy	uncrisp, leathery
bin	Kentish term for a large, round, picking basket, and later for a crib
bine	twining stalk or the whole top growth of the hop
bittering rate, value	*see* hopping rate
Black Country	heavily industrialized region of the West Midlands
blight	*see* aphids
bolting	sheaf of straw normally weighing 14 lbs but variable
booker	person responsible for keeping records of hops picked by each picker
bowler	chock to prevent wagon running backwards downhill
bract	individual sheath on the fruit containing the seed
burr	flower of the hop
bushel	dry or liquid measure of capacity equal to 8 gallons (36 litres)
catenary wire	support wire
charks	coke-like fuel produced from the sulphuric coal of the south-west Worcestershire coalfield; the term has also been used for charcoal and the 'dead' coal on the edge of a fire
cranked hook	hook with offset handle
crib	container into which the hops were picked. Sacking was stitched onto a wooden frame
cutting	pruning hop back to crown
didicoy	a travelling scrap dealer, etc., not a true gypsy; the name has also been used locally for gypsies and tramps
dobbin	workhorse
E.H.F.	Experimental Husbandry Farm
faggot	bundle of sticks bound together and used as fuel
fat hen	*chenopodium album*
flags	pieces of hop bine remaining on top wire after the bine has been pulled
FYM	farmyard manure
gapping up	replanting hops where previous ones had perished
greensack	sack into which hops were measured for transport to the kiln
grubbing	removing, digging out
half crib	crib with division in the middle for two separate pickers
hectare	10,000 sq metres or approx 2½ acres
hill	flat-topped mound on which the hop was grown
hogshead	54 gallons
hooker	long-handled tool, similar to a pruner, used for attaching hooks to the top wire
hop garden	*see* hopyard
hopping	hop picking
hopping rate	the proportion of hops used in brewing determined in lbs per barrel or grams per hectolitre
hopyard	hop field
house	section of hopyard
hurricane lamp	paraffin lamp with a glass covering to prevent the flame from being blown out
kell	kiln
kerf	stocker, spade-shaped drawhoe
kill	kiln
kiln hair	large mat of woven horsehair on which hops were placed for drying
leafing	removing the lower leaves on the bine, nowadays usually by chemical spray
Lent grain	spring wheat

megger	electrical instrument for measuring moisture content of hops while in the pocket
monkey	long rod to guide the string from peg to hook
mould	fungus disease
oasthouse	hop kiln
piece	bread and jam
plattens	perforated metal strips forming the bottom of a drying bin or kiln floor, which can be tilted by an external lever so that hops drop through between them for the next stage of drying
plenum chamber	part of hop kiln - the chamber below the drying floor
ploughing down	removing soil from hops back to the middle of the rows
ploughing up	returning soil to cover base of hops, to smother weeds and encourage strong cuttings
pocket	long sack, approx 6 ft. of closely woven jute into which hops are pressed and then marketed
polepuller	originally man who pulled the pole out of the ground in polework; after wirework was introduced the name was retained for men overseeing picking
polework	system of supporting hops on poles
quassia	bark or root used as an insecticide
reek	condition fault caused by too high a temperature, or too low an airspeed in the initial stages of drying when moisture will condense onto the hops giving them a dullish colour
roller hair	method to simplify emptying single tier kilns
rood	¼ acre
scuppet	wooden shovel for moving hops in the kiln
sett	cutting taken from a plant when cutting and throwing down, to be replanted perhaps in a nursery
shoddy	shredded rag
slag	sometimes known as basic or basic slag - waste material from blast furnaces applied as a phosphate fertilizer
slinger	unsupported pocket held only by ropes on a lorry load of hops
slipper	skid placed under one wheel of wagon to act as brake downhill
soller	loft, upper room
spiky, spiky heads	appearance of a growing tip suffering from downy mildew
spray	side shoot on which hops are produced
squat	to immobilize a wheel with a bowler or chock
stocking away	see throwing down
strig	stem of hop
tallet	hayloft
tatting cart	rag and bone man's handcart
throwing down	removing soil from around plants in spring, preparatory to cutting and tying
tines	slender prongs
tod, todd	unit of weight used for small load of wool etc. weighing 28 lb
top-hook	hook fixed to the top wire over which the hop string is run
treading hole	hole in hoproom or farmhouse floor from which a pocket was suspended for a man to tread hops into the pocket, before the advent of hand-operated mechanical presses
tumped	piled in heaps
wainhouse	shed for wagons and carts
wilt tolerant	resistant to verticillium wilt
wires	alternative word for bines
wirework	framework of permanent wires to support strings for hops to climb
zentner	50 kg or 110.23 lb

INDEX

Page numbers of illustrations, maps, diagrams, graphs and tables are in italics